MATHEMATICS OF SOFTWARE CONSTRUCTION

ALLAN NORCLIFFE
School of Engineering Information Technology, Sheffield City Polytechnic
GIL SLATER
Faculty of Science and Engineering, Manchester Polytechnic

ELLIS HORWOOD
NEW YORK LONDON TORONTO SYDNEY TOKYO SINGAPORE

First published in 1991 by
ELLIS HORWOOD LIMITED
Market Cross House, Cooper Street,
Chichester, West Sussex, PO19 1EB, England

A division of
Simon & Schuster International Group
A Paramount Communications Company

Printed and bound in Great Britain
by Hartnolls Limited, Bodmin, Cornwall

British Library Cataloguing in Publication Data

Mathematics of software construction.
Norcliffe, A. and Slater, G.
CIP catalogue record for this book is available from the British Library
ISBN 0-13-563370-2 (Library Edn.)
ISBN 0-13-563388-5 (Student Pbk. Edn.)

Library of Congress Cataloging-in-Publication Data available

HEMATICS OF
TWARE CONSTRUCTION

MATHEMATICS AND ITS APPLICATIONS
Series Editor: G. M. BELL,
Professor of Mathematics, King's College London, University of London

STATISTICS, OPERATIONAL RESEARCH AND COMPUTATIONAL MATHEMATICS Section
Editor: B. W. CONOLLY,
Emeritus Professor of Mathematics (Operational Research), Queen Mary College, University of London

Mathematics and its applications are now awe-inspiring in their scope, variety and depth. Not only is there rapid growth in pure mathematics and its applications to the traditional fields of the physical sciences, engineering and statistics, but new fields of application are emerging in biology, ecology and social organization. The user of mathematics must assimilate subtle new techniques and also learn to handle the great power of the computer efficiently and economically.

The need for clear, concise and authoritative texts is thus greater than ever and our series endeavours to supply this need. It aims to be comprehensive and yet flexible. Works surveying recent research will introduce new areas and up-to-date mathematical methods. Undergraduate texts on established topics will stimulate student interest by including applications relevant at the present day. The series will also include selected volumes of lecture notes which will enable certain important topics to be presented earlier than would otherwise be possible.

In all these ways it is hoped to render a valuable service to those who learn, teach, develop and use mathematics.

Mathematics and its Applications
Series Editor: G. M. BELL,
Professor of Mathematics, King's College London, University of London

Anderson, I. — **Combinatorial Designs: Construction Methods**
Artmann, B. — **Concept of Number: From Quaternions to Monads and Topological Fields**
Arczewski, K. & Pietrucha, J. — **Mathematical Modelling in Discrete Mechanical Systems**
Arczewski, K. and Pietrucha, J. — **Mathematical Modelling in Continuous Mechanical Systems**
Bainov, D.D. & Konstantinov, M. — **The Averaging Method and its Applications**
Baker, A.C. & Porteous, H.L. — **Linear Algebra and Differential Equations**
Balcerzyk, S. & Jösefiak, T. — **Commutative Rings**
Balcerzyk, S. & Jösefiak, T. — **Commutative Noetherian and Krull Rings**
Baldock, G.R. & Bridgeman, T. — **Mathematical Theory of Wave Motion**
Ball, M.A. — **Mathematics in the Social and Life Sciences: Theories, Models and Methods**
de Barra, G. — **Measure Theory and Integration**
Bartak, J., Herrmann, L., Lovicar, V. & Vejvoda, D. — **Partial Differential Equations of Evolution**
Bejancu, A. — **Finsler Geometry and Applications**
Bell, G.M. and Lavis, D.A. — **Statistical Mechanics of Lattice Models, Vols. 1 & 2**
Berry, J.S., Burghes, D.N., Huntley, I.D., James, D.J.G. & Moscardini, A.O. — **Mathematical Modelling Courses**
Berry, J.S., Burghes, D.N., Huntley, I.D., James, D.J.G. & Moscardini, A.O. — **Mathematical Modelling Methodology, Models and Micros**
Berry, J.S., Burghes, D.N., Huntley, I.D., James, D.J.G. & Moscardini, A.O. — **Teaching and Applying Mathematical Modelling**

Series continued at back of book

Table of contents

Preface

Aircraft manufacturers these days only build aeroplanes after producing precise designs and testing them rigorously. The same is true of car manufacturers and bridge builders. In fact this is the case with most makers of reliable, high performance products that have to be delivered on schedule and within budget.

Looking at how manufacturers produce their designs and test them, it is clear that in almost all cases the application of mathematics plays a central role. Some model of the product is created, typically using mathematics, and then by reasoning with this model, again using mathematics, the behaviour and performance of the product can usually be predicted in advance of construction. In this way initial designs are refined and specifications, which were agreed at the outset, are eventually satisfied. This engineering approach to design and manufacture has long been with us and, linked as it now is to the use of computers and sophisticated software, it has become the accepted method.

Recently this mathematically based approach has started to be used in the design and construction of software. There are many reasons for this, not least of which is the realisation that the old craft skills of programming, which are still a necessary part of the computing industry, are no longer sufficient by themselves for building software. Programs are becoming bigger and more costly to produce, software costs are typically outstripping hardware costs, and the demand is now for error-free quality software, that has been produced in a disciplined and managed way.

This is a book about the kind of mathematics that is needed in the construction of software, particularly the kind needed at the early stages of design. It is an introductory text which carefully explains the need for mathematics in the software development process, and which shows in clear and simple terms what this mathematics is and how it is used. Our aim is to provide you, our reader, whether you are an experienced programmer or just a beginner, with a thorough insight into the advantages to be gained from using mathematics, and to provide you with the motivation and means to become a more effective programmer.

The book is not high powered as far as the preknowledge that is required. Some familiarity with programming is assumed, but no deep knowledge of mathematics is necessary. Study of the subject to O-level, GCSE or BTEC equivalent is all that is needed. The book is aimed primarily at first and second year students in Higher Education, but will be of interest to sixth formers, and should be extremely valuable to many computer programmers already working in the software industry.

The need for the book stems from the uptake of mathematics that is beginning to occur in software engineering, and the accompanying shortage of texts in the area. Although formal methods of software construction are now taught on many computer courses, there are still few texts that can be used as an introduction to the subject. This lack of basic training material has been highlighted by the Alvey Directorate, and more recently by the Department of Trade and Industry, and both authors have been commissioned to develop video-based training packages in formal methods for programmers working in industry. The Alvey-funded "Essential Mathematics for Software Engineers" package and the DTI-funded "Z Readers Course" that have resulted, however, are relatively costly and out of reach of most students. A text that is at a fairly low level, that shows explicitly how to build models of software systems and reason formally about them, is urgently required. This book aims to fill such a need.

The mathematics required in the construction of software is discrete mathematics; the topics needed are sets, logic, functions, relations and proof. These are all presented in the following chapters in an integrated fashion, firmly within the context of the software development process. Each topic area is motivated via the use of relevant examples, and the aim is to present a balanced mix designed to illustrate points being made and the power of the mathematics developed. Most chapters have exercises and worked examples, so mathematical skills, as they are learned, can be practised and reinforced.

The notation we use adheres as closely as possible to the current Z notation. Z is fast becoming an industry-standard specification language and is ideally suited as a notation within which to present the ideas contained in this book. Z was developed at the Programming Research Group at Oxford University and the authors would like to acknowledge the Group for the notation that has emerged from it in recent years. We wish to point out, though, that this book covers only part of the Z notation; far more authoritative texts on Z exist for the advanced programmer or software engineer. The book will, however, suffice as an introduction to the ideas and notation that underpin Z, and readers should be well placed to move on to more advanced texts at a later stage.

The authors are indebted to the many people who have helped make this book a reality. They would like to thank all their colleagues for their helpful advice and comments, and the many students who have pointed out errors in early drafts and made suggestions for possible improvements. They are indebted to Sam Valentine for his useful comments on all of the chapters and for his advice on Z standards. The authors are particularly grateful to Audrey Hamnett who typed much of the text, and to Maggie Bedingham and Richard Gibson who so skillfully turned this text into camera-ready copy. Finally, they would like to thank Karen Rose at Ellis Horwood for her endless patience and constant encouragement.

Allan Norcliffe
Gil Slater

CHAPTER 1

Why mathematics?

1.1 INTRODUCTION

The case for using mathematics in software engineering is not immediately obvious. We can all cite instances of programs, written without the aid of mathematics, that have eventually worked perfectly, and we can all point to programmers in industry, whose backgrounds are non-mathematical, who certainly appear not to need mathematics. So just what is the case for using mathematics in the construction of software?

The case for mathematics can best be appreciated by looking at other longer-established disciplines, and how they have evolved. Let us look briefly at the discipline of civil engineering and in particular at bridge building. Bridges have been built for centuries and the first bridges were certainly not the product of mathematical analysis. They were built by a combination of experience, skill and craftsmanship, and many an ancient bridge is still standing today. These bridges were crafted more than engineered. However, as bridges became larger and more was expected of them, building methods had to change. More than just the wise application of skill and craftsmanship was needed, and slowly bridge building evolved to the engineering discipline it is today.

To build bridges that were safe under specified loadings, it became necessary to have a detailed understanding of the materials used in construction so that the behaviour of the assembled bridge could be predicted in advance and its performance thereby guaranteed. Engineers, therefore, began to work with the laws of science and to use the rules of mathematics. They very soon learnt to abstract away from the physical object, namely the bridge, to a model or representation of it, in order to calculate and reason formally about aspects of the structure before embarking on construction. Today it would be unthinkable to start building a large suspension bridge, for example, without similar preparation.

Thus, what happened to bridge building, in its evolution from a craft activity to an engineering discipline, is that the key ingredient of using theoretically-based mathematical analysis entered into the whole bridge-building process. Really, there is nothing special about bridge building and the evolution of car manufacturing, boat building, or aircraft construction can be traced similarly.

In contrast to these longer-established disciplines, software engineering is a young discipline. It has only been in existence for twenty years or so, considerably less time than computers themselves. It is at the early stages of its evolution and the software industry still relies heavily on the craft skills and experience of its programmers. Some would say that as a result of this we are currently experiencing a software crisis. But there is no disputing the steady, if unspectacular, progress made by software engineers towards improving the quality and productivity of the software development process.

However, escalating software costs and the need for ever more ambitious systems, still to be developed, all point to the fact that the long-established methods of building software are perhaps no longer sufficient to keep pace with demands. As with bridge building, new methods are needed. Already, in certain areas, mathematically-based techniques of analysis are slowly creeping into the design and construction of software, and seem set to become an integral part of the whole development process. But, growing though these areas are, the uptake and acceptance of mathematics by the entire software engineering community is far from complete. The software industry is at a painful transition stage. The discipline is at the turning point with regard to the use of mathematics that other longer-established disciplines passed long ago in their evolution; and it is likely to remain there for some time until hard evidence is produced concerning future benefits.

Thus, not surprisingly, the case for using mathematics in the construction of software is not immediately obvious. It was not obvious to the early bridge builders and neither was it obvious to those building the early flying machines. As we have stated, though, it would be unthinkable not to use mathematics in the building of a large suspension bridge or one of today's high-performance jet aircraft. Therefore, if we are ever to combat the software crisis effectively, and produce the error-free quality software that is being demanded, then the route is clear. There can be no alternative other than going down the road taken by the longer-established engineering disciplines, and bringing mathematics into far greater prominence in the whole software development process. The authors are firmly convinced of this, and the book is written on this assumption

1.2 THE TASK OF THE SOFTWARE ENGINEER

We have made repeated references to other engineering disciplines because these have been appropriate. However, it would be wrong at this stage to create the impression that the task of the software engineer is identical to that of the bridge builder. There are many differences and, indeed, the style of mathematics that each uses differs considerably. It is important, therefore, to look at what a software engineer does, so that we can appreciate how the use of mathematics can assist in the software development process.

The task of the software engineer is primarily to develop, build, and maintain software. Typically software engineers are engaged to develop and install new systems from scratch and to maintain existing ones by upgrading and modifying them. In developing programs, whether large or small, and irrespective of intended use, the stages involved are the same. Most software engineers recognise the following stages of development: requirements analysis, system specification, design, implementation, testing and maintenance. Let us look at each in turn.

Requirements analysis

When building anything it is important to find out exactly what is required. If we are building software for ourselves then the requirements analysis phase is fairly straightforward; we ought to know exactly what we want! Developing a system for a customer, however, is different. Effective communication must take place between software engineer and client and it is vital that both can agree on what the system has to do. All subsequent work depends on this phase of the development cycle, and it must be carried out thoroughly and carefully.

System specification

Having settled on what is required, the software engineer must then specify precisely what the software has to do to meet the requirement. A specification document is therefore produced. This document is referred to constantly at all subsequent stages of the development process. The specification acts as a blueprint for the system and models its actual behaviour. The essential feature of the specification is that it states what has to be done but not necessarily how it should be done. It gives the system designer the precision needed but allows the freedom to experiment with different designs. Specifications should be unambiguous and as free as possible of design detail or implementation directives. They should enable the developer and customer to reason precisely about the system, and should be concise enough to hide away unnecessary complexity.

Design

When customer and developer are satisfied that the specification reflects all the system properties and captures the required system behaviour, it is necessary to design data structures and algorithms to specify how things should be done. Here all the skill and experience of the systems designer come into play so that the specification can be implemented most efficiently. The designer must have a clear and unambiguous specification to do this.

Implementation

Having designed the data structures and algorithms, these must be coded in a programming language in such a way that the specification is implemented correctly. This requires considerable skill and experience on the part of the programmer. The key lies in using only those programming constructs that are well-understood; the analogue of bridge builders working only in materials with which they are familiar. Ideally the coding should follow from the specification in a series of steps which is guaranteed to preserve the constraints and conditions laid down in the specification. In this way correctness is built into the software as it is developed.

Testing

Testing of the software is carried out in order to establish that it performs and behaves as it should. Testing a program with carefully chosen data can certainly reveal errors, but cannot categorically verify that a program is correct with respect to its specification. Such a proof of correctness is often very difficult to give unless the development process has been significantly formalised. With stringent requirements on safety-critical systems such proofs are increasingly demanded. Testing the correctness of a program against its specification is known as verification. Establishing that the software behaves as it should is known as validation, and is quite different. A program could be verified as correct with respect to its specification, but if the specification is wrong the program is invalid.

Maintenance

After a system is installed, the role of the software engineer does not stop. As the system is used it may need to be modified or upgraded, sometimes after a long time interval. This maintenance is made easier if the original specification is available so that the knock-on effects of upgrading or modification can be fully established. In circumstances where only the program listings are available, maintaining the software is far from easy. Backtracking until a clear understanding is established of precisely how the software works is usually involved, and this can be costly.

Before leaving our consideration of what a software engineer does, it must be remembered that software has to be developed in a managed and controlled way. The software engineer must be able to plan ahead and predict such quantities as the size of the finished coding, how long the system will take to build, and how costly it is likely to be. Such measures, or metrics, are very important in project management. They are most easily obtained if the initial stages of the software development process have been carried out rigorously and if a complete and unambiguous specification is available.

In summary, then, the task of the software engineer demands more than just skill, craftsmanship and experience. The ability to be analytical is vital. Software engineers must be able to abstract away from the software they are building to a model of it. They must be able to reason with this model, predict from it, and evaluate their software against it. Now we consider how using mathematics can allow software engineers to do all of these things.

1.3 ADVANTAGES THAT MATHEMATICS CAN BRING

One of the most important documents that a software engineer produces is the specification. It models the behaviour of the system and is referred to constantly throughout the development process. The specification must be precise and unambiguous and ideally, therefore, it should be written in mathematics. Many specifications are written in English. However, expressive as English can be, the language is often ambiguous and open to different interpretations. Solicitors and lawyers, for example, spend much of their time sorting out different interpretations of the law because it is written in English. Systems designers or programmers cannot afford to spend too long interpreting a specification. They need to know what is required of the system being developed and must know precisely what the coding has to achieve. Thus a specification written entirely in English is really no longer adequate for many of today's needs.

The advantages that mathematics can bring at the specification stage follow directly from the properties of mathematics as a formal language.

- Mathematics is a precise language. There is no ambiguity. Mathematics gives the software engineer the precision needed.

- Mathematics is concise. Complex ideas can be expressed very succinctly in mathematics. Software engineers can hide away as much of the system complexity as they wish.

- Mathematics is expressively powerful. Very few ideas are incapable of being expressed in terms of mathematics.

- Mathematics facilitates formal reasoning. The consistency of what has been written can be tested using the rules of the language itself. The software engineer can test specifications for internal consistency and check whether any system constraints or other properties have been violated.

- Mathematics enables calculations to be performed. Via the rules of mathematics, system behaviour can be predicated in a formal way and the software engineer and customer can thus systematically check the appropriateness of a specification.

- Finally, mathematics is easily turned into code – more easily, for example, than English. Several mathematically-based specification languages can execute giving the software engineer all the advantages that rapid prototyping and animation can bring.

In addition to the advantages which mathematics offers at the specification stage, there are beneficial spin offs for the rest of the software development process.

- With a mathematical specification system designers know exactly what the system has to do. They can design data structures and algorithms with a clear knowledge of the criteria against which they are to be evaluated.

- The process of developing coding becomes more formalised and mechanical. With a precise specification every coding step can be checked systematically to see whether or not the specification has been met, and in this way correctness can be built into the program as it is being developed.

- Testing becomes more formal and less labour intensive. Using the rules of logic, it can be proved formally that a program matches its specification. Verification is therefore potentially a mechanical process, hopefully soon to be carried out by machines using program provers. Validation is also easier, as reasoning about the appropriateness of a system effectively amounts to contemplating the assumptions underpinning the mathematical specification.

- Maintenance of systems built using these formal methods should also be easier. For one thing, such systems will arguably be better designed and therefore more amenable to modification. Importantly, a mathematical specification will be to hand describing in precise detail how the system works. Time and money spent discovering such information will therefore be saved.

1.4 SPIN OFFS TO INDUSTRY AND TO THE PROGRAMMER

The advantages listed above are those that mathematics brings to the actual process of developing software. These advantages affect the software industry itself and also impact on the way in which the individual software engineer works. Let us consider the consequences for both the software industry and the programmer.

Formal methods and the software industry
To appreciate how formal methods affect the software industry it is instructive to look at the two graphs below. These give an indication of the resources needed at the various stages of software development using current working methods and using formal methods. The graphs are very approximate but data that are now becoming available bear out the overall features.

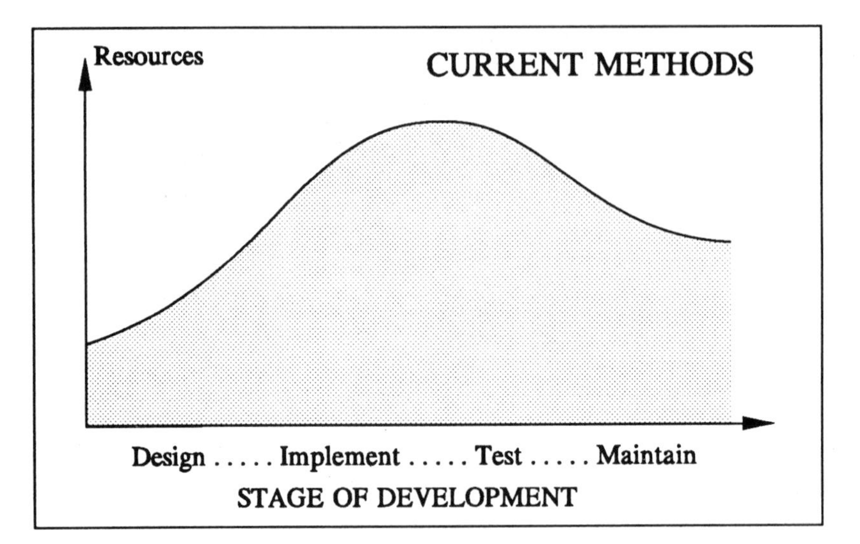

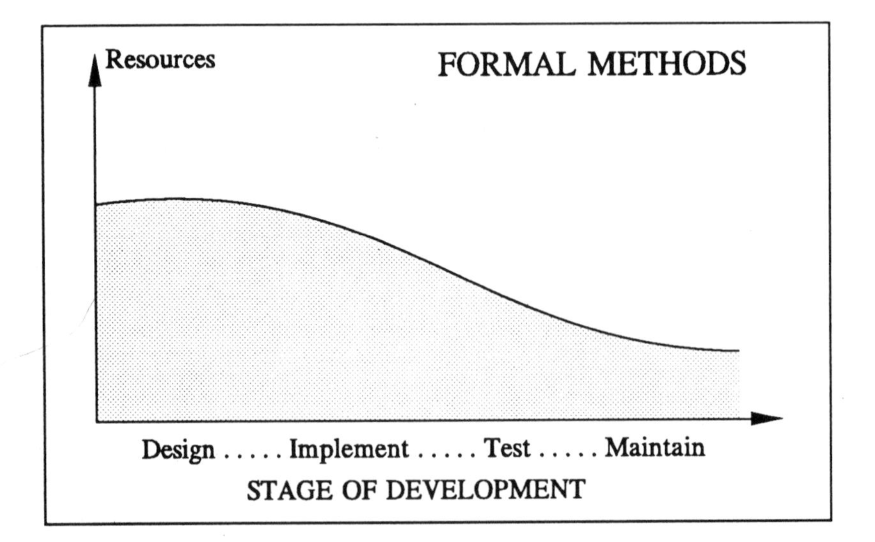

Figure 1.1 : Graphs showing the resources needed at the various stages of software development using current working methods and using formal methods

The first graph demonstrates that the software industry currently relies heavily on the craft skills and experience of its programmers. Vast resources are used employing programmers to check, rewrite and retest programs. Similarly a large amount of effort goes on discovering how installed systems work for the purposes of maintenance. This graph is symptomatic of working methods followed to assure quality via stringent acceptance sampling methods rather than by rigorous design and quality control procedures. This criticism may be unfair, but it is clear that the effort put in at the design stage is relatively small.

The second graph reveals different working methods. More effort is invested in the design stage. There is no denying that creating a formal specification, for example, takes more time than writing one in English. However, it will be seen that fewer resources are needed for testing the software, since it has been developed with built-in correctness as a feature. Maintenance needs fewer resources because a specification is already to hand.

So what overall conclusions can we come to? The total amount of resources needed (the area under the graph) is less when formal methods are used. This means, in effect, that the same quality can be achieved with fewer resources overall. Productivity is therefore improved with formal methods and any resources that are released can be used to enhance quality further. This all adds up to increased competitiveness and increased confidence that future demands on the software industry can be met.

Formal methods and the programmer

As yet most programmers working in industry do not use formal methods. Many have not been trained in the necessary mathematics to use formal methods, and many are actively putting off the evil day when they will have to grapple with this new technology! To those reading this book from such a position, and to those interested in learning about formal methods for real or just for fun, we can but recommend wholeheartedly to you this new way of developing programs.

By the time you reach the end of this book you will certainly know something about the mathematics of software construction. You will be starting to change the whole way you approach the problem of producing software. You will have started to think mathematically, using rigour and precision, rather than using the huge intuitive leaps which characterise software production as a craft. You will have learned to abstract away from the actual software that is to be developed to a model of it. You will be starting to reason about the software by manipulating this model as opposed to testing bits of coding. When you do start developing coding you will be thinking instinctively about how to prove that each bit of coding matches its specification. You will be thinking logically and rigorously about your work.

Most importantly, you will have at your disposal a formal language for effective communication – a language that will enable you to communicate efficiently with others skilled in the use of formal methods, and a language that facilitates precise communication with the lay person. Finally, although formal methods are still currently something of an unsettled technology, they are developing apace. Far better that you become part of this development than remain only an interested bystander.

1.5 THE KIND OF MATHEMATICS INVOLVED

Having convinced you of the desirability and need for mathematics in the construction of software, let us consider the kind of mathematics that is involved. It is very important to understand why we study the mathematics which follows, and it is very important to know intuitively why the mathematics needed by the software engineer is different from that used by the civil engineer.

In general, the kind of mathematics underpinning any engineering discipline reflects the nature of the discipline and, in particular, the properties of the systems that the engineer builds. Bridge builders construct systems whose properties depend continuously on such variables as mass, length and time. Stresses in structures and dynamical responses to inputs all vary this way. Bridges, therefore, are continuous systems and the style of mathematics that is needed to describe such systems is continuous mathematics. The civil engineer must thus study such topic areas as calculus and geometry. This is exactly the same mathematics that Newton developed to study the continuous motion of the planets in the solar system.

When we look at building software, however, we see that we are not constructing a continuous system. The software may well be that needed to control the operation of some continuous structure, like a bridge, but the software itself, and the means of reasoning about it, has little to do with continuous mathematics. Software is a discrete system. For example, it can only change in discrete amounts – by a line of coding, an additional variable name, a whole subprogram. There is no concept of software depending continuously on any of the entities that are a part of it. Software, therefore, when it is modelled using mathematics, involves discrete mathematics.

The specification, when written in terms of mathematics, involves such discrete mathematical structures as sets, functions and relations. These structures are joined by well–defined connectives to form predicates and statements that describe the operation of the software. The rules of logic can then be used to manipulate this formal description to predict and reason about the system. This all sounds straightforward and simple at this stage. Our aim is to show you that it remains so in practice.

1.6 THE ORGANISATION OF THE BOOK

The book has been organised to enable the reader to learn about the mathematics of software construction in a way that is natural, progressive and clear. Instead of presenting all the mathematics first, and then looking at applications later, we start the business of writing formal specifications just as soon as possible. The aim is to develop the mathematics progressively, all the time basing it around real and meaningful applications.

Once we have a working knowledge of the basis of set theory and logic, which is given in the next chapter, we set out the rules for writing specifications in terms of mathematics using the well-defined structure of a Z schema. This is done in Chapter 3. Chapters 4 and 5 develop the idea of a function in order to extend the structures available to us for writing specifications. Chapter 6 looks at a relatively large and open-ended problem to show how the ideas developed so far can be used. The important idea of partitioning a specification is brought to the fore, in order to show how system complexity can be managed and hidden away to keep the specification concise. This realistic application will highlight the need for further structures such as sequences and relations, and these are introduced and used in Chapters 7 and 8 respectively.

Chapter 9 then looks at the process of turning a specification into coding, and we look at how a specification, developed previously, is refined and systematically turned into a procedural program. In Chapter 10 we show how specifications can be tested for internal consistency and how coding might be checked for correctness against its specification. The further ideas of logic and proof that are needed for this are introduced as and when they are required.

In Chapter 11 we conclude our study of the mathematics of software construction by considering several more specifications from a range of contrasting areas. In Chapter 12 we reflect on what we have covered in the book and look at where formal methods are leading to in software engineering, highlighting achievements and difficulties, reporting on real applications, and discussing where more research work is needed.

CHAPTER 2

Getting started: sets and logic

2.1 INTRODUCTION

One fundamental property of all programs is that they manipulate information. Information comes in discrete amounts, from simple data items like names, numbers and lists to facts and rules involving these data. If we are to write specifications to model in precise and abstract terms what programs do, it follows that we need a precise and abstract way of describing information. This description is conveniently provided by the theory of sets and it is with this that we begin our study of the mathematics of software construction.

2.2 THE CONCEPT OF A SET

To establish what we mean by a set let us start by looking at the properties that sets possess.

Set properties

A set is a well-defined collection of distinct objects. These objects could be of any kind and are known as the elements of the set. A set containing the elements a, b and c is written as follows.

$$\{a,b,c\}$$

The notation is important. The general convention is to place curly brackets around the elements and to separate the elements from one another using commas. Thus the set containing the decimal characters 0 up to 9 could be written as

$$\{0,1,2,3,4,5,6,7,8,9\}$$

and the set containing the vowels as

$$\{a,e,i,o,u\}$$

where the assumption is that the identifiers *a, e, i, o, u* stand for the letters a, e, i, o, u of the alphabet. When writing out a set the order of the elements is of no significance. The set of vowels could equally well be written as

$\{e,a,u,i,o\}$

What is important is that we must be able to tell whether an element is a member of a set or not. When a set contains only a small number of elements then writing out all the elements inside curly brackets, as we have done here, is one way of enabling us to do this. There is a special notation that is used for set membership; this is the $\in$ symbol. To signify that the letter *a* belongs to the set of vowels, for example, we write

$a \in \{a,e,i,o,u\}$

To show that an element does not belong to a set we simply put a line through the $\in$ symbol. Thus, in the case of the letter *b*, we might write

$b \notin \{a,e,i,o,u\}$

In writing out a set, repeating any element does not create a new set. Repetitions are allowed, but there is no added information. Thus the set {1,1,3,2,2,3,3} is exactly the same as the set {3,1,2}, as the only distinct elements in each set are the numbers 1, 2 and 3.

Naming sets

It is clear from these properties that sets are defined once their elements are known. It is often convenient to give a set a name. Suppose we specifically want to define *Vowels* as the name of the set of vowels given by $\{a,e,i,o,u\}$. To do this we write

$Vowels == \{a,e,i,o,u\}$

The symbol == means "is defined to be", and so this statement reads that *Vowels* is defined to be the set containing the elements *a,e,i,o* and *u* where, again, the assumption is that the elements stand for the letters themselves.

Having named a set in this way we can refer to the set by its name. Several important sets that are used repeatedly in software engineering have come to have fixed names. We shall have need, for example, to use the following sets in writing specifications.

$\mathbb{N}$ the set of natural numbers containing 0,1,2,3,4,...
$\mathbb{Z}$ the set of integers containing ...,−3,−2,−1,0,1,2,3,...
$\mathbb{R}$ the set of all real numbers

A habit has also arisen amongst software engineers of using the name *CHAR* for the set of available characters on a standard keyboard. We, too, shall make use of this name in some of the specifications we write.

2.3 SUBSETS

A natural extension of the very important idea of a set is the notion of a subset. Suppose we have two sets A and B. If we can establish that every element of A is an element of B, then we say that A is a subset of B, and we write

$$A \subseteq B$$

Thus it is clear, for example, that the set $\{1,2,3\}$ is a subset of the decimal characters $\{0,1,2,3,4,5,6,7,8,9\}$. Thus

$$\{1,2,3\} \subseteq \{0,1,2,3,4,5,6,7,8,9\}$$

The empty set
One very important set, which is a subset of any set, is the set which has no elements in it at all, called the empty set. The empty set is written as

$$\{\ \} \quad \text{or} \quad \emptyset$$

and is just as important in set theory as the zero is in arithmetic.

Set equality
Suppose, having established that A is a subset of B, we also find that every element of B is in A. That is, both $A \subseteq B$ and $B \subseteq A$ are true. Then we say that sets A and B are equal and write

$$A = B$$

As an example of set equality, let A be the set of letters that make up the word *concurrent*, and B be the set of letters in the word *counter*. It is easily established that every element of A is in B and similarly that every element of B is in A, and thus

$$A = B = \{c,o,u,n,t,e,r\}$$

When two sets are not equal the symbol $\neq$ is used. The = symbol should not be confused with the == symbol. Their meanings are different.

Proper subsets

Before leaving subsets it is useful to consider what is meant by the term proper subset. If we have established that A is a subset of B, and we can find at least one element of B that is not in A, then we say that A is a proper subset of B. To signify that A is a proper subset of B we write

$$A \subset B$$

Writing $A \subset B$ does not bar us from also writing $A \subseteq B$ because all proper subsets are subsets. However, not all subsets are proper subsets so we cannot necessarily write $A \subset B$ knowing that $A \subseteq B$ is true. For example we can write

$$\{c,o,u,n,t,e,r\} \subseteq \{c,o,n,c,u,r,r,e,n,t\}$$

but the first set is not a proper subset of the second.

2.4 USING PREDICATES AND CONNECTIVES

The single most important property of a set is being able to tell if an element is a member of the set or not. When the set contains only a small number of elements, as in the examples so far, it is easy to decide whether a given element belongs to the set by simply checking it against set elements in turn. This can become tedious if the set contains a large number of elements, and is impossible if the set is infinite. A more convenient way of defining a set in such cases is to include, within the definition, the property that each element must satisfy to be a member of the set. Set membership can then be checked by testing a would-be element against this property.

Predicates

The defining property for set membership is called a predicate. The notation $p(x)$ stands for "x satisfies property p". This may be incorporated into a different way of writing sets as follows.

$$\{ x \mid p(x) \}$$

This notation reads "the set of elements x such that the predicate $p(x)$ holds". The vertical line separating x and the predicate $p(x)$ stands for "such that". Thus the set of odd natural numbers, for example, could be written as

$$\{ x \mid x \in \mathbb{N} \text{ and } x \text{ is odd} \}$$

When the predicate is tested with a particular x value to see if x is in the set, the predicate will be either true or false. If it is true, then x belongs to the set; if it is false, then it does not. Thus

$$4 \notin \{ x \mid x \in \mathbb{N} \text{ and } x \text{ is odd } \}$$
$$7 \in \{ x \mid x \in \mathbb{N} \text{ and } x \text{ is odd } \}$$

Readers familiar with the Z specification language may have noted the absence of type declarations in this new way of writing sets. Strictly speaking type declarations are needed in set definitions to prevent anomalies such as Russell's Paradox. Type declarations are, of course, a part of Z and will be used in definitions once types and declarations have been introduced in Chapter 3. For the time being we continue to develop the concepts of set theory in a rather informal way in order to keep things simple. The study of Z assumes a knowledge of set theory and the aim of this chapter is to provide this knowledge. From Chapter 3 onwards we adhere fully to the Z notation.

Connectives

If we look at the defining predicate in the example just given, we see that it is made up of two simpler predicates, namely the predicate $x \in \mathbb{N}$ and the predicate x is odd, joined by the word "and". This word "and" is an example of a logical connective. Useful connectives for creating predicates out of simpler ones are the words "and", "or" and "not". Their counterparts in mathematics are respectively the symbols $\wedge$, $\vee$ and $\neg$. In order to be precise about what these symbols mean, we specify their meaning using truth tables.

Truth tables

The truth table for "not", ie for the symbol $\neg$, is the following.

$p(x)$	$\neg p(x)$
T	F
F	T

The connective $\neg$ simply reverses the truth values T (true) and F (false) when applied to a predicate.

The truth tables for "and" ($\wedge$) and "or" ($\vee$) are given below. There are now four possible combinations of truth values to consider, because $\wedge$ and $\vee$ each involve two predicates $p(x)$ and $q(x)$.

$p(x)$	$q(x)$	$p(x) \wedge q(x)$	$p(x) \vee q(x)$
T	T	T	T
T	F	F	T
F	T	F	T
F	F	F	F

Using these truth tables, we can evaluate mechanically any predicate, provided the predicate involves no connectives other than $\wedge$, $\vee$, and $\neg$. We shall see that other connectives can be expressed in terms of these three and so, in principle, it is possible to establish set membership from the defining predicate, no matter how complicated the predicate.

2.5 SET OPERATIONS

It is important to remember that programs are usually written to work for a whole set of possible input values and not just for one or two fixed values. Similarly, when in use, programs usually produce a whole set of possible outputs as opposed to certain fixed values. Sets, therefore, are a fundamental structure, vital when it comes to describing program inputs and outputs in a specification. We have just seen how the defining predicates for sets can be built up from simpler predicates using connectives. In like manner the sets we might require in a specification can be built up from simpler sets using standard set operations which we now consider.

Set intersection

If we have two sets A and B, then elements that are in both A and B make up what is known as the intersection of A and B. This set is illustrated as the shaded area in the set diagram below.

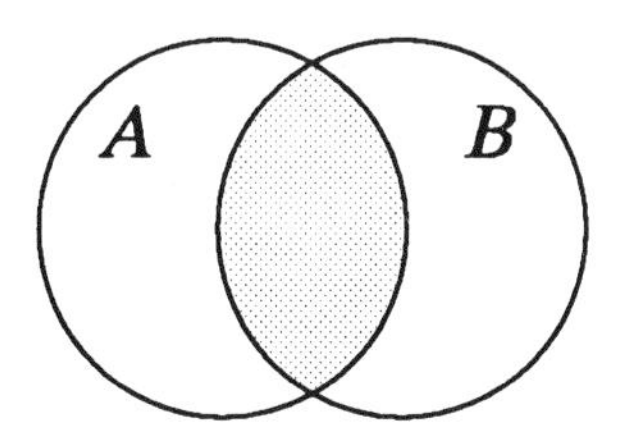

Figure 2.1 : Set intersection

We write this intersection set as

$A \cap B$

The symbol $\cap$ is a new symbol known as the intersection operator. A valid predicate that may be used to define this intersection set is the following.

$$A \cap B = \{ x \mid x \in A \wedge x \in B \}$$

It follows that if $p(x)$ is the predicate that defines the set property for A, and $q(x)$ is the predicate for B, then the predicate for $A \cap B$ will be $p(x) \wedge q(x)$. Also, because of the way $A \cap B$ is defined, it is obvious that $A \cap B$ is the same set as $B \cap A$ and thus

$$A \cap B = B \cap A$$

Sets that have no elements in common have as their intersection the empty set { }. Such sets are called disjoint. On the other hand, if A is a subset of B, then the intersection set will just be the smaller set A.

Set union

Suppose, again, that we have two sets A and B. Elements that are in A or B, or both sets, make up what is called the union of the sets A and B. The union of A and B is illustrated in the set diagram by the shaded area.

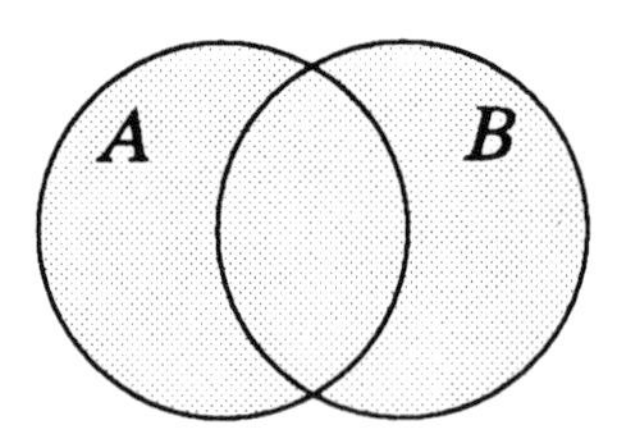

Figure 2.2 : Set union

The set is written as

$A \cup B$

The operator $\cup$ is the union operator and a valid predicate to define $A \cup B$ is

$$A \cup B = \{ x \mid x \in A \vee x \in B \}$$

In terms of the defining predicates $p(x)$ and $q(x)$ for the sets A and B respectively, it follows that the corresponding predicate for $A \cup B$ is just $p(x) \vee q(x)$. It is also clear that $A \cup B$ is the same set as $B \cup A$, so

$$A \cup B = B \cup A$$

The union of two sets can only be the empty set if both sets are empty; if A happens to be a subset of B, then the union set will be the larger set B.

Set difference

Given our two sets A and B, the elements in A that are not in B make up the shaded set shown in the diagram.

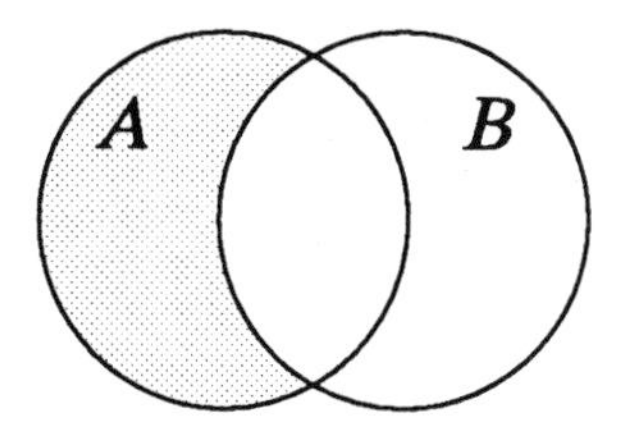

Figure 2.3 : Set difference

This set is a difference set and is written as

$$A \setminus B$$

The set $B \setminus A$, which is the set of elements in B that are not in A, will in general be different from $A \setminus B$. A valid predicate that may be used to define the set difference $A \setminus B$ is the following.

$$A \setminus B = \{ x \mid x \in A \wedge \neg(x \in B) \}$$

The defining predicate for $A \setminus B$ is thus the predicate $p(x) \wedge \neg q(x)$, where $p(x)$ and $q(x)$ have their usual meaning. Clearly if A and B are disjoint sets, then $A \setminus B = A$ and $B \setminus A = B$.

Set operations are useful when specifying how various operations in a program are to work. For example, the set union operator enables us to specify how elements might be added to a set, and the set difference operator enables us to specify how elements might be removed.

Cardinality

We have spoken rather loosely about large sets and small sets, and need to be specific about what we mean. The number of elements in a finite set is known as its cardinality. The cardinality operator is represented by the symbol #, so the size of a set A can be written as

$$\#A$$

Obvious meaningful examples are $\#Alphabet = 26$, $\#Vowels = 5$. With reference to the set diagram below, and assuming both sets are finite, it is also obvious that

$$\#(A \cup B) = \#A + \#B - \#(A \cap B)$$
$$\#(A \cup B) = \#(A \setminus B) + \#(B \setminus A) + \#(A \cap B)$$

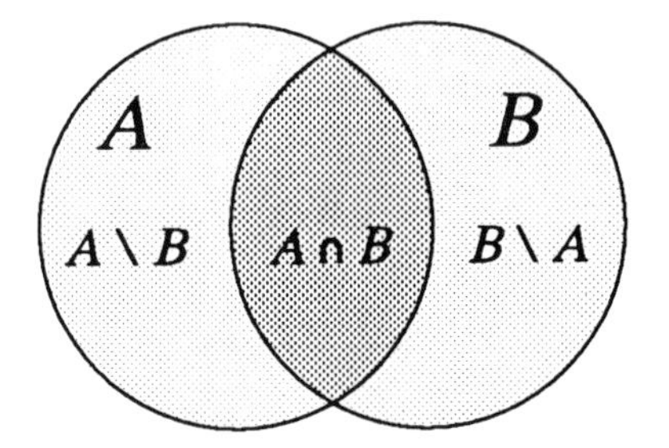

Figure 2.4 : Cardinality of the set $A \cup B$

The results follow directly by counting the respective set elements and accounting for them all correctly. The cardinality operator is useful in specifications.

2.6 STRUCTURED OBJECTS

We have defined what is meant by a set and seen how to build new sets from sets that have already been defined. To model all the situations that are likely to occur when writing specifications, it is important to have to hand sets with more structure than is permitted by the notation so far developed. We need to have available power sets and Cartesian products.

Power sets
The power set of a set is the set of all its subsets. The mathematical notation for the power set of A is

$$\mathbb{P}\ A$$

A valid predicate that may be used to define the power set of A is the following.

$$\mathbb{P}\ A = \{\ X \mid X \subseteq A\ \}$$

The power set of a set can be written out explicitly when the set is finite. For example, if $A = \{a,b,c\}$ then

$$\mathbb{P}\ A = \{\{\ \}, \{a\}, \{b\}, \{c\}, \{a,b\}, \{b,c\}, \{a,c\}, \{a,b,c\}\}$$

The number of elements in the power set grows exponentially as the number of elements in the set. If $\#A = N$, then it will be seen that $\#\mathbb{P}\ A = 2^N$, as every one of the N elements in A has two possibilities – either being in a subset or not. Thus the cardinality of a power set is usually large compared to the cardinality of the original set.

Cartesian products

A set is a structure where the order of its elements is unimportant. With many objects that we may have to describe in software engineering, some form of ordering may be necessary. For example, a data item may have to consist of a name, followed by a date of birth, followed by an address. How can we use sets to model such situations? Cartesian product sets provide the answer.

Given two sets A and B, the set of ordered pairs (a,b), where a belongs to A and b to B, makes up the Cartesian product set of A with B. The notation used for the Cartesian product of A with B is

$$A \times B$$

A valid predicate that defines this Cartesian product set is the following.

$$A \times B = \{\ (x,y) \mid x \in A \wedge y \in B\ \}$$

Since we are dealing with sets of ordered pairs then, in general, $A \times B \neq B \times A$. There is nothing special about only two sets being involved in a Cartesian product. We can form the Cartesian product of as many sets as we wish. Instead of ordered pairs being involved, we have sets of n-tuples. For the Cartesian product $A \times B$, providing each set is finite, it is easily seen that

$$\#(A \times B) = \#A * \#B$$

where the * symbol is being used to represent multiplication.

2.7 WORKED EXAMPLES

Example 1 : Simple set properties

This first example is designed to reinforce the understanding of simple set properties and to illustrate set operations such as union, intersection, and difference.

- If A is the set of letters in the word "software", and B is the set of letters in the word "hardware", then

  (a) write out the sets corresponding to
  - (i) $A \cap B$.
  - (ii) $A \cup B$
  - (iii) $A \setminus B$
  - (iv) $B \setminus A$
  - (v) $(A \setminus B) \times (B \setminus A)$

  (b) obtain the values of
  - (i) $\#\mathbb{P}\ B$
  - (ii) $\#(A \times B \times B)$
  - (iii) $\#\mathbb{P}((A \cap B) \times (B \setminus A))$

Solution (a)
(i) It is clear that B is the set $\{h,a,r,d,w,e\}$ and therefore
$A \cap B = \{s,o,f,t,w,a,r,e\} \cap \{h,a,r,d,w,e\} = \{w,a,r,e\}$

(ii) $A \cup B = \{s,o,f,t,w,a,r,e\} \cup \{h,a,r,d,w,e\} = \{s,o,f,t,w,a,r,e,h,d\}$

(iii) $A \setminus B = \{s,o,f,t,w,a,r,e\} \setminus \{h,a,r,d,w,e\} = \{s,o,f,t\}$

(iv) $B \setminus A = \{h,a,r,d,w,e\} \setminus \{s,o,f,t,w,a,r,e\} = \{h,d\}$

(v) $(A \setminus B) \times (B \setminus A)$ is the set $\{s,o,f,t\} \times \{h,d\}$, which is $\{(s,h),(s,d),(o,h),(o,d),(f,h),(f,d),(t,h),(t,d)\}$.

Solution (b)
(i) The set B has 6 elements in it, so the power set of B will have 2^6 (ie 64) elements in it. Thus $\#\mathbb{P}\ B = 64$.

(ii) $\#(A \times B \times B)$ will be the number of elements in A multiplied by the number of elements in $B \times B$. The number of elements in $B \times B$ is the square of the number of elements in B. Thus $\#(A \times B \times B) =$ $\#A * \#B * \#B = 8*6*6 = 288$.

(iii) The set $A \cap B$ has 4 elements in it and the set $B \setminus A$ has 2. The set $(A \cap B) \times (B \setminus A)$ thus contains 4*2, ie 8 elements. The power set of this set will therefore contain 2^8 elements, which is 256.

Example 2 : General set properties
This second example is designed to establish some important properties of the union, intersection and difference operators. We often have need to reason formally about sets, and these general set properties will be useful.

- If A, B and C are three arbitrary sets establish, using set diagrams, the following identities

(i) $A \cap (B \cup C) = (A \cap B) \cup (A \cap C)$
(ii) $A \cup (B \cap C) = (A \cup B) \cap (A \cup C)$
(iii) $(A \setminus B) \cap C = (A \cap C) \setminus (B \cap C)$
(iv) $(A \setminus B) \cup C = (A \cup C) \setminus (B \setminus C)$

Solution
(i) The set $A \cap (B \cup C)$ is the intersection of A with $B \cup C$. This set is represented on the set diagram by the doubly shaded area:

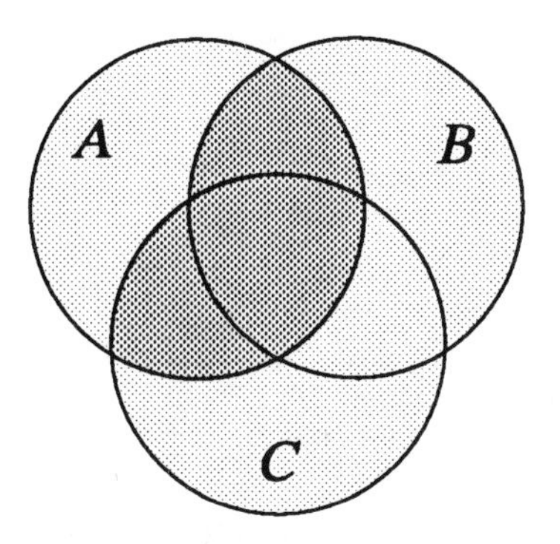

Figure 2.5 : The set $A \cap (B \cup C)$

The set $(A \cap B) \cup (A \cap C)$ is the set made up of either type of shading:

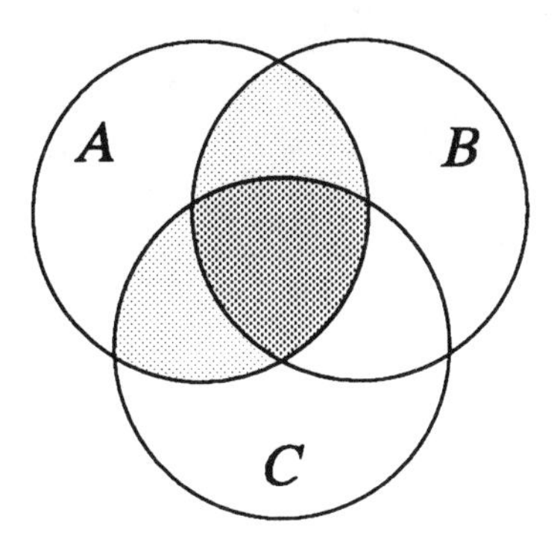

Figure 2.6 : The set $(A \cap B) \cup (A \cap C)$

The two sets in each of the above diagrams are the same and the identity to be established therefore holds.

(ii) The set $A \cup (B \cap C)$ is the union of A and $B \cap C$. This is the set made up of either type of shading in the diagram:

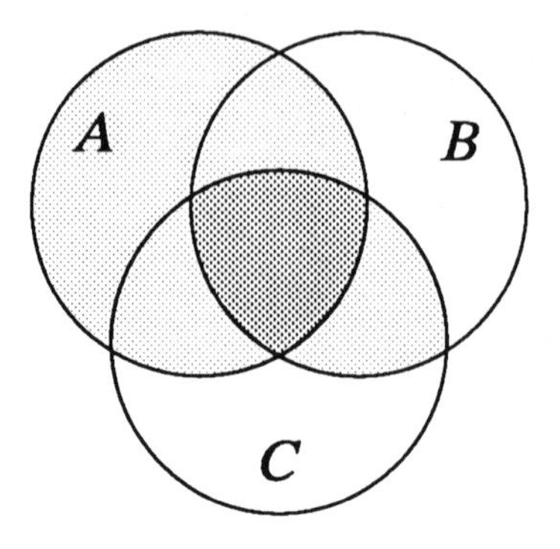

Figure 2.7 : The set $A \cup (B \cap C)$

The set $(A \cup B) \cap (A \cup C)$ is the doubly shaded set:

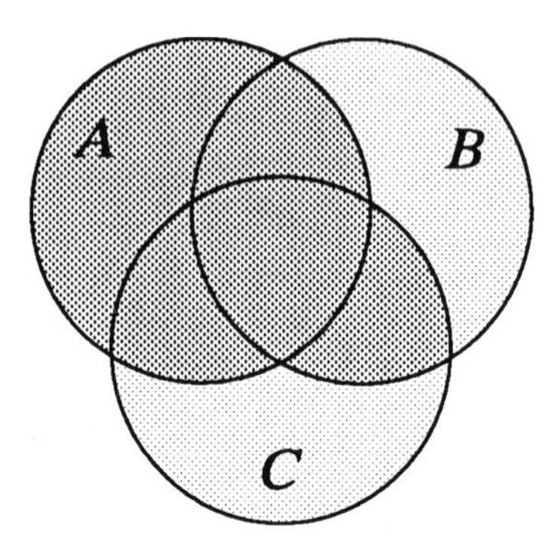

Figure 2.8 The set $(A \cup B) \cap (A \cup C)$

The two sets shown in both diagrams are the same, thus establishing the identity.

(iii) $(A \setminus B) \cap C$ is the set represented by the doubly shaded area in the diagram:

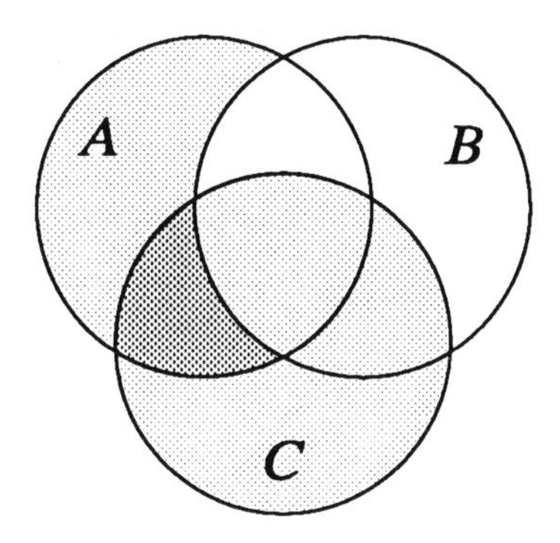

Figure 2.9 : The set $(A \setminus B) \cap C$

$(A \cap C) \setminus (B \cap C)$ is the set shaded as shown:

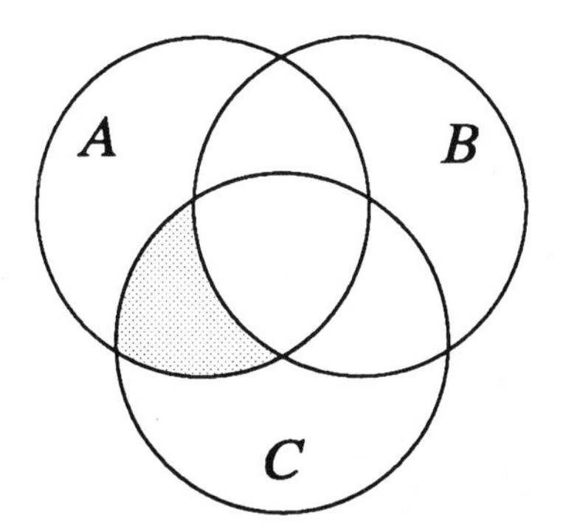

Figure 2.10 : The set $(A \cap C) \setminus (B \cap C)$

As the two sets in the diagrams are the same we can conclude that the identity holds.

(iv) $(A \setminus B) \cup C$ is the set shown made up of any shading:

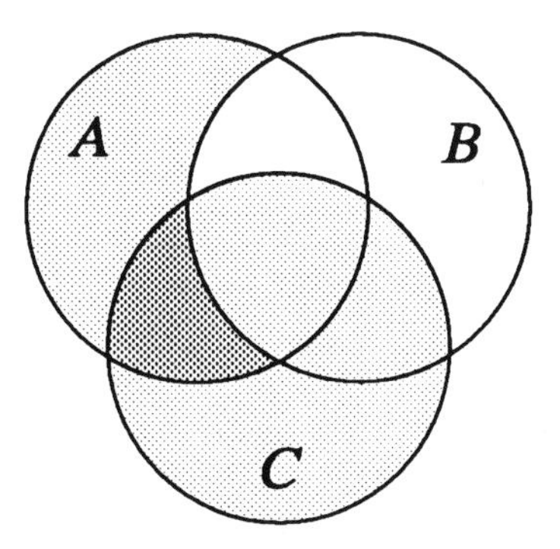

Figure 2.11 The set $(A \setminus B) \cup C$

The set $(A \cup C) \setminus (B \setminus C)$ is the shaded set shown:

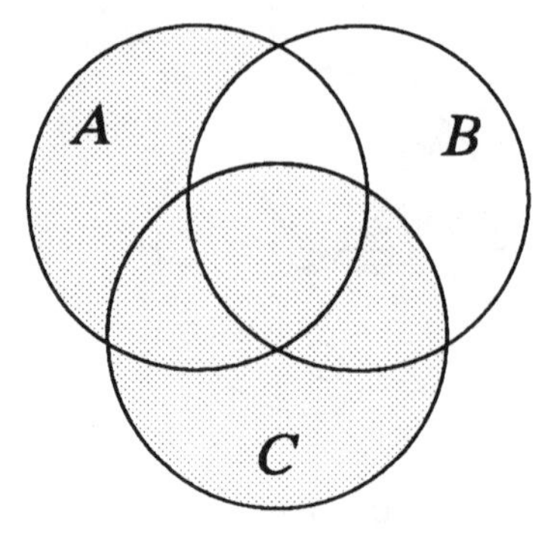

Figure 2.12 : The set $(A \cup C) \setminus (B \setminus C)$

Once again, the two sets are the same and so the identity to be established therefore holds.

Example 3 : Predicates and truth tables
This example enables us to see how the truth tables we have listed may be used to evaluate predicates and how DeMorgan's laws may be established.

- (a) Evaluate the truth value of the predicate given by $((x>2) \vee (x>-3)) \wedge (x<8)$ in the following cases
  (i) $x = 0$
  (ii) $x = 10$
  (iii) $x = -4$
  (iv) $x = 4$

  (b) Establish DeMorgan's laws by showing, for arbitrary predicates $p(x)$ and $q(x)$, that
  (i) $\neg(p(x) \wedge q(x)) = \neg p(x) \vee \neg q(x)$
  (ii) $\neg(p(x) \vee q(x)) = \neg p(x) \wedge \neg q(x)$

Solution (a)
(i) If $x = 0$, then the truth value of $((x>2) \vee (x>-3)) \wedge (x<8)$ will be that of the expression
$((0>2) \vee (0>-3)) \wedge (0<8)$
ie $(F \vee T) \wedge (T)$
Using the truth tables for $\vee$ and $\wedge$ we obtain
$(F \vee T) \wedge (T) = T \wedge T = T$

(ii) In a similar way, we have for $x = 10$
$((10>2) \vee (10>-3)) \wedge (10<8) = (T \vee T) \wedge (F) = T \wedge F = F$

(iii) For $x = -4$, we have

$$((-4>2) \vee (-4>-3)) \wedge (-4<8) = (F \vee F) \wedge (T) = F \wedge T = F$$

(iv) For $x = 4$, we have

$$((4>2) \vee (4>-3)) \wedge (4<8) = (T \vee T) \wedge (T) = T \wedge T = T$$

Solution (b)

(i) To establish that the first of DeMorgan's laws is true we list out the truth values of both sides of the identity, for all different combinations of the predicate values of $p(x)$ and $q(x)$, and show that they are the same.

$p(x)$ $q(x)$	$p(x) \wedge q(x)$	$\neg(p(x) \wedge q(x))$	$\neg p(x) \vee \neg q(x)$
T T	T	F	F
T F	F	T	T
F T	F	T	T
F F	F	T	T

Since the truth tables for the expressions in columns 3 and 4 are the same it follows that the first of DeMorgan's laws is true, so that $\neg(p(x) \wedge q(x)) = \neg p(x) \vee \neg q(x)$.

(ii) We similarly establish that $\neg(p(x) \vee q(x)) = \neg p(x) \wedge \neg q(x)$ by showing that their two truth tables are the same.

$p(x)$ $q(x)$	$p(x) \vee q(x)$	$\neg(p(x) \vee q(x))$	$\neg p(x) \wedge \neg q(x)$
T T	T	F	F
T F	T	F	F
F T	T	F	F
F F	F	T	T

Since the truth tables of $\neg(p(x) \vee q(x))$ and $\neg p(x) \wedge \neg q(x)$, given in columns 3 and 4, are the same it follows that the second of DeMorgan's laws is true.

Example 4 : Modelling using sets

This example is designed to demonstrate the power of the notation we have developed so far for the purposes of software specification. It also demonstrates how to reason formally about what is written, using the established properties of sets.

- As part of a security system in operation in a building only known staff are allowed to enter the building. They are checked in during the morning and checked out when they leave. Using the set theory ideas developed so far, capture the essential properties of the system and specify, as tightly as you can, the checking in and checking out operations. Check that these operations preserve the properties of the system.

Solution

Let us begin by defining some sets. Let *users* be the set of known staff who are allowed to enter the building. Let *in* be the set of staff who have been checked into the building, and let *out* be the set of staff who have yet to be checked in or who have been checked out of the building. Clearly the essential features of the system require that

$$in \cup out = users$$
$$in \cap out = \{\ \}$$

These conditions we shall call the system data invariant. Suppose a person, namely *staff*, wishes to be checked in; we obviously require that the following condition is true.

$$staff \in out$$

If this is true, then we can check the person into the building. This checking in process has the following side effects. The set *in* will change to *in'*, where

$$in' = in \cup \{staff\}$$

and *out* will change to *out'*, where

$$out' = out \setminus \{staff\}$$

Similarly, suppose *staff* wishes to be checked out; then *staff* should have been checked in, if not to be an intruder, so we require

$$staff \in in$$

The side effects of this operation can now be specified as follows.

$$in' = in \setminus \{staff\}$$
$$out' = out \cup \{staff\}$$

To check that these two operations, as specified, preserve the data invariant we must now show formally that for each operation

$in' \cup out' = users'$
$in' \cap out' = \{\ \}$

We shall only do this for the checking in operation; the proof for the checking out operation is left to the reader as an exercise. For checking in we have

$$in' \cup out' = (in \cup \{staff\}) \cup (out \setminus \{staff\})$$
$$= (out \setminus \{staff\}) \cup (in \cup \{staff\})$$

Using the result of worked example 2 (iv) of this chapter this latter expression can be written as

$$(out \cup (in \cup \{staff\}) \setminus (\{staff\} \setminus (in \cup \{staff\}))$$
$$= ((in \cup \{staff\}) \cup out) \setminus (\{staff\} \setminus (in \cup \{staff\}))$$
$$= (in \cup (\{staff\} \cup out)) \setminus \{\ \}$$
$$= (in \cup (out)) \setminus \{\ \}$$
$$= users \setminus \{\ \}$$
$$= users$$

Similarly we have that

$$in' \cap out' = (in \cup \{staff\}) \cap (out \setminus \{staff\})$$
$$= (out \setminus \{staff\}) \cap (in \cup \{staff\})$$

Using, now, the result of worked example 2 (iii), this latter expression is

$$(out \cap (in \cup \{staff\})) \setminus (\{staff\} \cap (in \cup \{staff\}))$$
$$= ((out \cap in) \cup (out \cap \{staff\})) \setminus ((\{staff\} \cap in) \cup \{staff\})$$
$$= (\ \{\ \} \cup \{staff\}) \setminus (\ \{\ \} \cup \{staff\})$$
$$= \{staff\} \setminus \{staff\}$$
$$= \{\ \}$$

The system data invariant is thus preserved by the checking in operation, as required. This gives us confidence in our specification, showing that, as defined, the checking in operation is at least internally consistent.

2.8 EXERCISES

1. Using the sets

$A = \{jack, jill, den, sue, bill\}$
$B = \{jill, sue, andy, kylie\}$
$C = \{jack, jill, den, andy\}$

determine the following.

(a) (i) $A \cap B$ (ii) $A \cup B$ (iii) $B \cap C$
(iv) $(A \cap B) \cup (B \cap C)$ (v) $(A \cup B) \setminus (B \cap C)$
(vi) $((A \cap B) \cap C) \cup (A \cap C)$

(b) (i) $\mathbb{P}\ C$ (ii) $\#(A \times B)$ (iii) $\#((A \times B) \setminus (B \times A))$

2. Use diagrams to show that the following special cases are true

$A \setminus B = \{\ \}$ if and only if $A \subseteq B$
$A \setminus B = B$ if and only if $A = B = \{\ \}$
$A \setminus B = A$ if and only if $A \cap B = \{\ \}$

3. Given the predicate $((x \leqslant y) \wedge (y < z)) \vee (\neg(x+y < z))$, where x, y, z are natural numbers, establish the truth value of the statements generated with the following values of x, y and z

(i) $x = 5$ $y = 1$ $z = 3$
(ii) $x = 5$ $y = 5$ $z = 5$
(iii) $x = -2$ $y = 1$ $z = 1$

4. When can $A \times B = B \times A$?

CHAPTER 3

Developing ideas: schemas

3.1 INTRODUCTION

We have now at our disposal the basic mathematical notation that we need to begin writing formal specifications. Writing a formal specification is essentially the same as constructing a mathematical model. Building any model is a creative activity, which people often find daunting because of the imaginative leaps in intuition that are sometimes needed. Obviously the more systematic and methodical we can be when developing a specification the easier the task becomes. To help in this respect we use the specification language known as Z, and use the tried and tested approaches and structures that are part of this language.

Z is a formal notation that was developed at the Programming Research Group at Oxford University. It is fast becoming an industry standard and enables specifications to be written in a systematic, methodical and rigorous fashion. The language caters for all the usual mathematics of sets, logic and functions but also contains a distinctive structure known as a schema. A Z schema is a well-defined mathematical structure that can be manipulated formally and is an integral part of a specification.

In this chapter we look specifically at how schemas are structured and how they are written. We start by establishing some Z notation, looking initially at the very important concept of a type.

3.2 TYPES

In most model building exercises we start by defining the quantities that are involved in the problem. We might well make statements like "let x be the number of rolls of wallpaper needed" or "let the mass of the person on the ladder be m". By these statements we are effectively assigning types to variable names. Here the quantity x is being defined to be an integer and the variable m a mass, and so on.

When writing a specification in Z the same kind of defining process occurs. Computer languages such as Pascal or FORTRAN have built in data types like integers, reals, and logical variables. Z does not have any built in types for the simple reason that it is a specification language, and a specification language should not bias the designer towards particular data types. However, Z does allow designers to choose their own data types and to use the rules of mathematics to construct new ones from these types. In Z types are nothing more than sets; but not all sets that we might define are types. The idea is that any element or data item involved in a specification should belong to exactly one type.

An example will help to illustrate this point. Consider the set of decimal characters that we met in the previous chapter. For simplicity let us call this set *decimal*. Instead of regarding each of the ten decimal characters to be of type *decimal*, it is far more sensible to think of the set $\mathbb{Z}$ of integers as the basic type to which individual decimal characters belong. Thus, whilst *decimal* is itself a set, it is not a type, but a subset of the type $\mathbb{Z}$.

In deciding whether a set is a type this subset property is obviously useful. However, it is important to remember that it is the writer of the specification who ultimately decides which sets are to be types and which, therefore, are to be subsets. Types in Z are of two kinds: basic types and constructed types.

Basic types

Basic types in Z are the types out of which constructed types are built. Basic types are sets containing atomic elements, in other words, elements that possess no property other than that they belong to the basic type set. The easiest way of introducing basic types into a specification is to define them to be types out of the blue. The process is sometimes called parachuting and to signify that $\mathbb{Z}$ and *CHAR*, for example, are to be regarded as basic types, we simply write their names inside square brackets as follows.

$$[\mathbb{Z}, CHAR]$$

In general, if we wish to parachute the basic types $T_1,T_2,\ldots,T_n$ into a specification, we write

$$[T_1,T_2,\ldots,T_n]$$

The only requirement is that we introduce the basic types into the specification before the sets are actually referred to.

Another way of introducing a basic type into a specification is to define the type explicitly via a free type definition. Thus if we want to use a basic type called *GRADE*, and we know that the elements of *GRADE* are to be the seven grades α, $\alpha-$, $\beta+$, β, $\beta-$, $\gamma+$, γ, then we would make the following free type definition:

$$GRADE ::= \alpha \mid \alpha- \mid \beta+ \mid \beta \mid \beta- \mid \gamma+ \mid \gamma$$

All that this new notation is telling us is that any element in *GRADE* has to be either an α, an $\alpha-$, a $\beta+$, a β, a $\beta-$, a $\gamma+$, or a γ. Again, the only requirement is that we should supply the definition of the basic type before its use in the specification is required.

Constructed types

Once basic types have been introduced into a specification they can then be used as building blocks to form constructed types. There are three kinds of type constructors in Z: set types, Cartesian product types and schema types. Let us consider each in turn.

- Set types are used to specify the type of any sets that we may want to use in a specification. Set types involve the power set notation. Thus suppose, in a specification, we want to use a set of telephone numbers called *phones*. If these telephone numbers are each instances of some basic type *PHONE*, then it is clear that *phones* will be a subset of the set *PHONE*. The set *phones* will thus be an element from the power set of *PHONE* and its type is therefore defined to be the set type written as $\mathbb{P}\ PHONE$. In general, any set of objects of the same type T is itself an object with the set type $\mathbb{P}\ T$.

- Cartesian product types are used to specify the type of objects such as ordered pairs, triples or n–tuples. Thus if x is of type T_1 and y of type T_2 then the pair (x,y) will be of type $T_1 \times T_2$. Similarly the n–tuple $(x_1,x_2,\ldots,x_n)$, where x_1 is of type T_1, x_2 of type $T_2,\ldots$, and x_n of type T_n, will be of type

  $$T_1 \times T_2 \times \ldots \times T_n$$

  A date of birth in the form (dd,mm,yy) could therefore be regarded as being of type

  $$DAY \times MONTH \times YEAR$$

- Schema types, as their name suggests, are used to specify objects in a specification that are themselves schemas. More will be said about them after schemas have been introduced and used.

3.3 DECLARATIONS

Objects of interest in a specification can be introduced by declaring them as instances of a type. This is done in a well–defined way. Thus, if objects with names a, b, and c are all of type T, we write out their declaration as follows.

$a, b, c : T$

Clearly a specification may involve many variable names and several types. A list of declarations, separated by semicolons or placed on new lines, makes up what is called a signature. A typical signature might therefore appear in a specification as follows.

$$a, b, c : T_1 \; ; \; d : T_2$$
$$e, f : T_1 \times T_2$$
$$g : T_3 \; ; \; h : \mathbb{P}\, T_1$$

It is important to note that the order in which we write the declarations is of no significance. Also, whilst it is usual to declare variables as instances of types directly, it is quite admissible, providing no confusion arises, to declare variables as instances of sets that are themselves subsets of types. For example, knowing that *decimal* is the set of positive integers less than 10, and therefore of type $\mathbb{P}\,\mathbb{Z}$, a positive integer less than 10, called *dec*, could be declared conveniently as follows.

$dec : decimal$

Thus the declaration for specifying how two natural numbers are added to form a third might be written as

$first\_no, second\_no, result : \mathbb{N}$

Before we look at how these ideas are used in the writing of schemas, let us consider briefly how declarations are incorporated into the writing of sets in Z.

3.4 WRITING SETS IN Z

The basic assumption in Z is that a set can only contain elements of the same type. Thus, if a set $\{a,b,c\}$ is used in a Z specification, a, b and c must be of the same type. This fact is explicit when the predicate notation is used. The standard predicate notation in Z for a set of elements from a set T, containing elements of the same type, with defining property p, is the following.

$$\{ x : T \mid p(x) \}$$

The type of elements in a set can be quite complex and involve constructed types. To facilitate the writing of such sets, the following set comprehension notation in Z is useful.

$$\{ x_1 : T_1 \; ; \; x_2 : T_2 \; ; \; \ldots \; ; \; x_n : T_n \mid p(x_1, x_2, .., x_n) \bullet t \}$$

This stands for the set of elements t, that involve the variables x_1 from set T_1, x_2 from set T_2, ..., x_n from set T_n, with defining predicate p.

Thus, if we wanted to define the Cartesian product set $A \times B$, where elements of A are from the set X, and those of B are from the set Y, then we could do this conveniently as follows.

$$A \times B = \{ a : X ; b : Y \mid a \in A \wedge b \in B \bullet (a,b) \}$$

3.5 SCHEMAS

So far we have said that a schema is a well-defined mathematical structure that is an integral part of a specification. Instead of trying to describe a schema further, let us have a look at a simple example.

```
┌─Subtract──────────────────────────
│ first_no    : ℕ
│ second_no   : ℕ
│ result      : ℕ
├───────────────────────────
│ first_no  ≥  second_no
│ first_no  =  second_no + result
└───────────────────────────────────
```

This is a schema which specifies the conditions that are necessary for one natural number to be subtracted correctly from another to furnish a result that is, itself, a natural number. Clearly this is a trivial problem, but it is ideal for our purposes, as it allows us to concentrate on the features of the schema without worrying about the difficulties of the problem area.

We see that a schema is indeed a well-defined structure. The first important point to note is the fact the schema has a name. This one is called *Subtract*. Most schemas have names, thus enabling them to be referred to in other schemas. Secondly we should note that the schema has a dividing line. Above this dividing line is the signature of the schema, where all the data items and quantities used in the schema are declared and thereby identified. Below the dividing line are the predicates that specify how the quantities and data items must be related to achieve the purpose of the schema.

Here, therefore, we are declaring that the quantities of interest in the schema are three natural numbers: *first_no*, *second_no*, and *result*. In the predicates section of the schema we state what we know must apply, and that is that *first_no* should not be smaller than *second_no* for the subtraction to be possible. To ensure that the result of the subtraction is correct, we also state that *result* when added to *second_no* must equal *first_no*. Notice that nowhere does the schema include any statement as to how the subtraction should be carried out. All we have done is specify what must be true for the subtraction to be possible and for the result of the subtraction to be correct.

In general, then, we see that the structure of a schema is as follows.

```
┌─Name──────────────────────────────
│ declarations
├──────────────────
│ predicates
└───────────────────────────────────
```

When predicates are written on new lines, as in our *Subtract* schema, the assumption is that they are joined by the "and" connective. All the logical connectives that we have met so far can be used in the predicates section of a schema.

An equivalent representation of the *Subtract* schema is thus

```
┌─Subtract──────────────────────────
│ first_no, second_no, result : ℕ
├──────────────────
│ (first_no ≥ second_no) ∧
│ (first_no = second_no + result)
└───────────────────────────────────
```

The overriding consideration should be to keep schemas as simple and compact as possible, consistent with preserving clarity and preventing any ambiguity.

3.6 SPECIAL CONVENTIONS

In Z a special convention is adopted for the names of data items that are used in a schema. If a variable is to be used as an input in a schema then its name would normally include a final query mark. Thus the name written as

$x?$

would signify that $x?$ was an input to the operation being specified. Similarly if a variable is used in a schema as an output then its name would contain a final shriek mark. The name written as

$y!$

would signify that $y!$ was an output from an operation.

Thus, adopting this convention, our schema for carrying out subtraction could have been written as follows.

```
┌─Subtract──────────────────────────────
│ first_no?, second_no? : ℕ
│ result! : ℕ
├───────────────────────
│ first_no? ≥ second_no?
│ first_no? = second_no? + result!
└───────────────────────────────────────
```

Not all data items in a schema need be inputs or outputs. Many are what are called state variables. These variables typically describe the state of some particular system of interest. Again there is a special notation that is adopted for these variables. Variables that represent initial (or before) states of a system are left undecorated, whilst variables that represent final (or after) states are decorated with a prime. Consider the following schema.

```
┌─CoinIn────────────────────────────────
│ display, display' : ℕ
│ coinvalue? : ℕ ; sound! : ℕ × ℕ
├───────────────────────
│ coinvalue? ∈ {1,2,5,10}
│ sound! = (5,250)
│ display' = display + coinvalue?
└───────────────────────────────────────
```

This schema models the successful operation of inserting a coin into a vending machine. The state of the vending machine is represented by a state variable called *display* that is a natural number. Typically, *display* will be showing the value zero, and only when the machine is being used will its value change. A coin, modelled by the input *coinvalue?*, is inserted into the machine. The machine only accepts 1p, 2p, 5p, or 10p coins, so *coinvalue?* has to be a member of the set {1, 2, 5, 10} for the operation to be successful. To signify that the operation is successful, two things happen. First of all the machine plays a note which is modelled by the output variable *sound!* This variable is of Cartesian product type and its value of (5, 250) signifies that a note of frequency 250 Hertz is to play for 5 hundreths of a second. A note in the region of middle C is therefore sounded. Secondly, the value of *display* changes to *display'*. The after state value, *display'*, becomes equal to the sum of the before state value, namely *display*, together with the value of the coin.

3.7 SCHEMA OPERATIONS

All the schemas we have written so far have been extremely short and simple, but as a result easy to comprehend and read. It would be a pity if schemas written to specify realistic systems were more lengthy and complicated. To prevent this from happening there are several operations that we can perform on schemas to hide away the complexity that always arises when dealing with real problems.

Schema inclusion

Complexity can be hidden away by using schema inclusion. Schema inclusion enables us to refer to and use other schemas within a given schema. To see how schema inclusion works, consider worked example 4 of Chapter 2, where the problem was that of specifying a system for logging staff in and out of a building as part of a simple security system. Instead of writing one schema to specify the totality of the logging in or logging out operation, we separate out the description of the state of the system from the description of the operation itself and write two schemas, with one referencing the other.

Firstly we write the schema that describes the state of the system of staff identity codes involved. Using the sets that we defined previously, and assuming that the basic type *STAFF_ID* has been parachuted into the specification, this schema can be written as follows.

```
─State──────────────────────────
│ in, out, users : ℙ STAFF_ID
├──────────────────
│ in ∩ out = { }
│ in ∪ out = users
└───────────────────────────────
```

The checking in operation is then specified via the following schema.

```
─CheckIn────────────────────────
│ State
│ State'
│ staff? : STAFF_ID
├──────────────────
│ staff? ∈ out
│ in' = in ∪ {staff?}
│ out' = out \ {staff?}
│ users' = users
└───────────────────────────────
```

This schema has included within it the schema called *State*. To include a schema within another all we do is to include its name within the declarations part of the schema. This is equivalent to including all the declarations and predicates of the schema we are wishing to include. The predicates are automatically conjoined to those of the including schema with the logical "and" connective. The *CheckIn* schema also includes the decorated schema *State'*. When a schema is decorated the variables in the declarations and predicates part become decorated. Including a decorated schema within another is a quick way of bringing into scope all the after–state names that we might require when specifying an operation that alters the state of a system.

The predicates in *CheckIn* specify the conditions that must be satisfied when a member of staff successfully checks into the building. Notice that schema inclusion has allowed much of the detail to be hidden away in the specification of the checking in operation. It has also enabled us to partition the problem, thus reducing its complexity and facilitating a more systematic approach.

The Δ and Ξ notation

Operations like the *CheckIn* operation above change the internal state of systems on which they operate. To signify that an operation could change the state of a system it is usual to make use of the Δ (pronounced delta) notation in Z. The Δ notation does two things. Firstly it alerts the reader that the operation could change the internal state of the system, but it also brings into scope the appropriate before and after states of the system. The Δ notation is used in the following way. If S is any state schema, then ΔS is the schema containing both S and S' as shown.

```
┌─ΔS──────────────────────
│ S
│ S'
└─────────────────────────
```

If ΔS is now included in any operation schema it therefore automatically brings into scope the before and after states of the system described by S and S', together with their associated predicates.

Thus, in the security system example, instead of including *State* and *State'* in the *CheckIn* schema we could have included just one schema called *ΔState* as shown.

```
┌─CheckIn─────────────────
│ ΔState
│ staff? : STAFF_ID
├─────────────────
│ staff? ∈ out
│ in' = in ∪ {staff?}
│ out' = out \ {staff?}
│ users' = users
└─────────────────────────
```

Not all operations, of course, change the state of a system. If an operation does not have any side effects as far as the system state is concerned, this fact is signified using the Ξ (pronounced xi) notation in

Z. If S is the name of the system state schema, then including ΞS in an operation schema makes available any system states needed by the operation, but signals that there are no side effects as far as state variables are concerned.

Thus, if we wanted to query our security system state to find out what current user identity codes there were in the system, we would make use of the Ξ notation as follows in the specification of such a querying operation.

$$
\begin{array}{|l}
\textit{QueryForUsers} \\
\hline
\Xi State \\
users! : \mathbb{P}\ STAFF\_ID \\
\hline
users! = users \\
\hline
\end{array}
$$

The output, *users!*, is simply set equal to the current value of *users* held by our system.

Once again, via precise notation, we are hiding away detail but still conveying all the information needed. Further examples illustrating this notation in use are covered in the worked examples.

Schema disjunction

We can conveniently build schemas from schemas by joining them together with logical connectives. To illustrate schema disjunction, or the use of the $\vee$ connective, let us consider the *Subtract* schema again. Notice that this schema only specifies the conditions needed for the successful subtraction of two natural numbers. It does not say what is to happen if the condition that the first number is bigger than the second number is violated. In these circumstances, perhaps, we would like some message reported to the user. A schema to do this can easily be written and it might be the following one called *SubtractError*.

$$
\begin{array}{|l}
\textit{SubtractError} \\
\hline
first\_no?\ ,\ second\_no? : \mathbb{N} \\
message! : REPORT \\
\hline
first\_no? < second\_no? \\
message! = subtraction\_not\_possible \\
\hline
\end{array}
$$

Between them *Subtract* and *SubtractError* cover all possibilities with regard to the two inputs *first_no?* and *second_no?* In other words either *Subtract* will apply, or *SubtractError* applies. To cater for all possibilities we need a schema that combines these two by putting the declarations together (without repeats) and joining their respective predicates by the logical "or" connective. If this schema is called

RSubtract, meaning robust *Subtract*, then the following formal definition does this. The symbol ≙ means "is defined to be".

$RSubtract \mathrel{\hat{=}} Subtract \lor SubtractError$

Joining schemas this way is known as schema disjunction and is a well defined way of constructing new schemas from ones already written. Schema disjunction allows us to partition a problem into manageable chunks and then assemble schemas in a formal way later on.

Schema conjunction
Schemas can be joined using the "and" connective. If we see written down

$S \mathrel{\hat{=}} S_1 \land S_2$

where S, S_1 and S_2 are schemas, then S will be a schema with the following properties. The declarations in S will be the combined declarations of S_1 and S_2 (again without repeats) and its predicates will be those of S_1 conjoined with those of S_2 via the $\land$ connective. Thus S, as defined here, is exactly the same as the schema that includes S_1 and S_2. In other words, schema conjunction and inclusion are essentially the same schema operation.

3.8 WORKED EXAMPLES

Example 1 : Using the schema calculus
In our first worked example we show how schema conjunction and disjunction together may be used to specify a robust user interface for a particular operation.

- Specify a robust subtract operation which incorporates suitable reporting mechanisms for indicating whether or not the operation has been successful.

Solution
First of all we define a schema called *Success* that has the simple output message *ok* of type *REPORT*.

```
┌─Success──────────────────────────
│ message! : REPORT
├──────────────────
│ message! = ok
└──────────────────────────────────
```

The robust interface is then created out of the *Subtract* and *SubtractError* schemas, that we met when looking at schema disjunction, in conjunction with the *Success* schema we have just defined. This is done by redefining the *RSubtract* schema as follows.

$$RSubtract \mathrel{\widehat{=}} (Subtract \wedge Success) \vee SubtractError$$

Thus, if the condition $first\_no? > second\_no?$ is satisfied in *Subtract*, then the operation is carried out and the message *ok* is reported. If the condition is not met, then it must be the case that $first\_no? < second\_no?$ applies and the message *subtract_not_possible* is reported. The *RSubtract* operation caters for all eventualities, reports accordingly, and is therefore robust. It has the desirable property that it now furnishes a report, whatever the outcome, and does not just signal an error.

Example 2 : Setting up an initial state schema
This example shows how an initial state of a system may be specified.

- For the simple security system considered earlier, specify an initial state of the system that satisfies the predicates of the state schema.

Solution
An initial state of the system, called *InitState*, may be specified as follows.

```
┌─InitState──────────────────────────
│ State
├────────────────────
│ in = { }
│ out = { }
│ users = { }
└────────────────────────────────────
```

Clearly this assignment of the empty set to each of the state variables sets up an initial state with no user identity codes in it. The initial state is a valid state of the system as the predicates of *State* are satisfied by this initialisation.

It is worth noting that it is quite common in Z specifications to use the prefix *Init* to signify an initial state.

Example 3 : Using the Δ convention
In this example we see the Δ notation being used.

- Specify (a) the *CheckOut* operation in the simple security system and (b) specify the operation for adding a new user identity code to the system.

Solution

(a) The operation for checking out a member of staff from the building and updating the system state accordingly may be specified as follows.

```
┌─CheckOut──────────────────────────
│ ΔState
│ staff? : STAFF_ID
├───────────────────
│ staff? ∈ in
│ in' = in \ {staff?}
│ out' = out ∪ {staff?}
│ users' = users
└───────────────────────────────────
```

Clearly, for a checking out operation to work properly the staff identity code must belong to the set *in*. In other words the staff member must be in the building. The condition expressed as *staff*? ∈ *in* is the schema precondition. If this is satisfied then *staff*? is taken out of *in* and put in *out*. The set *users* remains unchanged by the *CheckOut* operation.

(b) The operation for adding a new user identity code to the system can be specified in several ways. The way we have chosen to specify it here assumes two things. Firstly it is assumed that the new member of staff has been issued with a staff identity code prior to the *Add* operation. Secondly it is assumed that the new identity code is added to the set *out*, so that if the staff member subsequently wishes to enter the building they will have to invoke the *CheckIn* operation. The *Add* operation is therefore specified as follows.

```
┌─Add───────────────────────────────
│ ΔState
│ new? : STAFF_ID
├───────────────────
│ new? ∉ users
│ in' = in
│ out' = out ∪ {new?}
│ users? = users ∪ {new?}
└───────────────────────────────────
```

Example 4 : Building robust user interfaces

In this final example we construct robust interfaces for certain operations in the simple security system.

- In the context of the simple security system, give a specification of (a) a robust *Add* operation and (b) a robust *CheckIn* operation

Solution

(a) In anticipation of the error messages that we may wish to report in the error handling schemas of robust interfaces we define a free type called *REPORT* as follows.

$$REPORT ::= ok \mid already\_user \mid already\_in \mid not\_known \mid already\_out \mid still\_in$$

We also define a *Success* schema as before, namely

```
┌─Success──────────────────────────
│ message! : REPORT
├──────────────────
│ message! = ok
└──────────────────────────────────
```

Noting that the precondition for the *Add* operation is $new? \notin users$, then it follows that *Add* will not work if the negation of this precondition applies, namely if $new? \in users$. We can therefore define a robust *Add* operation as follows

$$RAdd \mathrel{\hat=} (Add \land Success) \lor AlreadyUser$$

where the *AlreadyUser* schema will have as its precondition the condition $new? \in users$. The *AlreadyUser* schema can be specified to give as output the message *already_user* in the following way.

```
┌─AlreadyUser──────────────────────
│ ΞState
│ new? : STAFF_ID
│ message! : REPORT
├──────────────────
│ new? ∈ users
│ message! = already_user
└──────────────────────────────────
```

(b) The robust *CheckIn* operation can be specified at the schema level as follows.

$$RCheckIn \mathrel{\hat=} (CheckIn \land Success) \lor CheckInError$$

However, when the precondition for *CheckIn*, which is $staff? \in out$, is violated then either $staff? \in in$ is true or $staff \notin users$ is true. Thus it makes sense to define *CheckInError* as follows in terms of two new schemas.

$$CheckInError \mathrel{\hat=} StaffIn \lor NotUser$$

These new schemas will respectively have preconditions given by $staff? \in in$ and $staff? \notin users$, and output messages to match. Their specification may be given as follows.

```
┌─StaffIn──────────────────────────
│ ΞState
│ staff? : STAFF_ID
│ message! : REPORT
├──────────────────
│ staff? ∈ in
│ message! = already_in
└──────────────────────────────────
```

```
┌─NotUser──────────────────────────
│ ΞState
│ staff? : STAFF_ID
│ message! : REPORT
├──────────────────
│ staff? ∉ users
│ message! = not_known
└──────────────────────────────────
```

3.9 EXERCISES

1. Give a specification of the operation that removes a staff identity code from the system state in the case of the simple security system. Assume that the code can only be removed after the staff member has been checked out of the building.

2. Write robust operations for checking a user out of the building and for removing a staff identity code from the system.

3. Write robust querying operations that give as output

   (a) the set of identity codes of users in the building
   (b) the set of identity codes of users out of the building
   (c) the set of identity codes of users of the building

CHAPTER 4

Functions

4.1 INTRODUCTION

The specifications written so far have used sets, power sets, and Cartesian products. Another very important construct, which is used extensively in formal specifications, is the mathematical object known as a function. A simple example of where a function might be used is in the modelling of a telephone directory. Given a person's name we know that a directory can be used to furnish the person's telephone number. The operation of such a directory could be specified by using a function. Given the person's name as input, the function would return, as output, the person's telephone number.

Essentially, a function is a structured object involving ordered pairs of the kind (*input*,*output*). In this chapter we look in detail at the structure of a function and at its component parts.

4.2 THE CONCEPT OF A FUNCTION

A function is nothing more than a set of ordered pairs of the kind (*input*,*output*) where unique outputs are associated with given inputs.

The following set of ordered pairs, which represents a telephone directory with just four entries in it, is a simple example of a function.

$$\{\ (tom,123456),\ (dick,123467),\ (harry,123456),\ (pat,123478)\ \}$$

The uniqueness property is satisfied by this set because associated with any name is one and only one telephone number. Note, however, that the uniqueness property does not prevent people having the same telephone number. The ordered pairs involving *tom* and *harry*, for example, contain the same telephone number. So in general, whilst unique outputs have to be associated with given inputs, the opposite does not have to be true: unique inputs do not have to be associated with given outputs.

There are two important sets associated with a function:

- a set called the domain, which is the set of acceptable inputs to the function
- a set called the range, which is the set of possible outputs from the function

Let us consider each of these in turn.

The domain
The domain is the set of inputs for which the function is defined. The domain of a function called f is written as

dom f

Brackets may be used to avoid ambiguity, so dom(f) is an acceptable way of writing the domain of a function f. The domain is a subset of a usually larger set known as the source of the function. The source is any convenient set known to contain the domain and in many cases is taken as the type set to which elements of the domain belong.

Thus, in our simple example, if the telephone directory function is called *dir*, then the set of names listed in the actual directory make up dom *dir*. Therefore

dom *dir* = {*tom*, *dick*, *harry*, *pat*}

This set of names will be a subset of a larger set of people's names, and thus the source of *dir* could conveniently be taken to be the type set *NAME*, for example.

The range
The range set is made up from the outputs associated with elements of the domain. If x is an input value in dom f then the corresponding element in the range set is written as

$f\ x$

Again brackets may be used to prevent any ambiguity that might arise, so the range element could therefore be written as

$f(x)$

The range set, itself, is written as

ran f or ran(f)

The range is a subset of a usually larger set called the target of the function. The target is any set known to contain the range, and is often taken to be the type set to which all elements of the range belong. Thus in our directory example the range is the set given by

$$\text{ran } dir = \{ 123456, 123467, 123478 \}$$

whilst the target could be taken to be the set $\mathbb{N}$ or the type set $\mathbb{Z}$.

4.3 KINDS OF FUNCTION

There are several different kinds of function. A convenient way of classifying functions is to regard them as either partial functions or as total functions.

Partial functions

A partial function is the most general kind of function, in the sense that all functions are partial. If a function f takes an input from its source X and produces an output belonging to its target Y, then f is said to be a partial function of form

$$X \pfun Y$$

It is declared in any signature by writing

$$f : X \pfun Y$$

Thus in our telephone directory example we could declare the function *dir* as follows.

$$dir : NAME \pfun \mathbb{N}$$

If we declare a function to be partial we are signifying that there may be some subset of the source for which the function is not defined.

Total functions

If we happen to know that a function is defined for all its source, so that dom f is equal to the source, we say that the function is a total function. In terms of its source X and its target Y a total function f is declared using the following signature.

$$f : X \longrightarrow Y$$

An example of a total function would be a function called *sum* that takes two natural numbers as input and returns their sum as output. Its signature would be

$sum : \mathbb{N} \times \mathbb{N} \longrightarrow \mathbb{N}$

The type of a function

Given that any expression appearing in a Z specification has to belong to just one type set, a natural question to ask is what is the type set to which a particular function belongs.

Since functions are sets of ordered pairs it is clear that power sets as well as Cartesian products are going to be involved. Suppose, then, that A is the type set to which elements in the domain of our function belong, and B is the type set containing elements in its range. The set of pairs that makes up the function will thus be one of the elements in the power set of $A \times B$. It follows, therefore, that the type set to which the function belongs is the constructed type

$$\mathbb{P}(A \times B)$$

Thus, for example, our telephone directory function, *dir*, will be of type

$$\mathbb{P}(NAME \times \mathbb{Z})$$

A declaration of the kind

$$dir : \mathbb{P}(NAME \times \mathbb{Z})$$

could certainly be used to introduce *dir* into a specification, but it is preferrable to use the special notation that we have introduced for declaring partial functions and write

$$dir : NAME \rightarrowtail\!\!\!\!\!+ \ \mathbb{Z} \quad \text{or} \quad dir : NAME \rightarrowtail\!\!\!\!\!+ \ \mathbb{N}$$

In general it is good practice to convey as much information as we can in any declaration; that is why, for example, a different notation is used to distinguish between total and partial functions.

4.4 WRITING FUNCTIONS

There are many ways of writing out the definition of a function. In this section we consider different ways in which the *input,output* pairs, that make up the function, can be specified. These include direct enumeration of the pairs, explicit definition of the rule that relates an input to an output, and implicit definition of the rule. To write function definitions requires some new notation, so we start by considering this.

Special notation

Function definitions involve specifying how outputs are related to inputs for all inputs belonging to the domain of the function. We therefore need to have a formal way of writing "for all" and, on occasions, of being able to write "there exists". The quantifiers of predicate logic enable us to do this.

Quantifiers

The two quantifiers of predicate logic are the universal quantifier and the existential quantifier. The universal quantifier, which means "for all", is represented by the symbol

$$\forall$$

and the existential quantifier, which stands for "there exists", is written

$$\exists$$

In mathematics these symbols are used as follows

quantifier signature | predicate • predicate

or simply as

quantifier signature • predicate

Thus, to say "for all account numbers x in the domain of the function *balance*, *balance*(x) should not be negative" we would write

$$\forall\ x : ACC\_NO \mid x \in \mathrm{dom}(balance) \bullet balance(x) \geq 0$$

or simply

$$\forall\ x : \mathrm{dom}(balance) \bullet balance(x) \geq 0$$

The vertical line means "such that", as in the set notation that we met earlier in Chapter 2, and the fat dot here means "then". Thus translated literally the first expression above reads "for all x of type *ACC_NO*, such that x belongs to the domain of *balance*, then *balance*(x) is greater than or equal to zero". The second expression, which says the same thing, only more simply, reads "for all x in the domain of *balance*, then *balance*(x) is greater than or equal to zero".

In order to say "there exists an account number y in the domain of the function *balance*, where *balance*(x) is positive", we use the existential quantifier as follows.

$$\exists\ y : ACC\_NO \mid y \in \mathrm{dom}(balance) \bullet balance(y) \geq 0$$

As before, if we do not mention the type set *ACC_NO* explicitly, we can simplify the expression slightly by writing

$\exists\ y : \mathrm{dom}(balance) \bullet balance(y) \geq 0$

Here the fat dot, when used in conjunction with the existential quantifier, means "where".

We can mix both types of quantifier in the same statement. Thus

$\forall\ x,y : \mathbb{N} \bullet \exists\ z : \mathbb{N} \bullet z \leq x + y$

reads "for all x and y belonging to the natural numbers, then there exists a natural number z, where z is less than or equal to x plus y".

The implication connective

There are many occasions when a statement is required of the kind

if $p(x)$ then $q(x)$

where $p(x)$ and $q(x)$ are both predicates. For example we may wish to make the following statement concerning accounts at a bank.

if $x \in \mathrm{dom}(balance)$ then $balance(x) \geq 0$

Formally we write "if $p(x)$ then $q(x)$" as follows.

$p(x) \Rightarrow q(x)$

The symbol $\Rightarrow$ is called the implication connective and is very important in formal reasoning and inference. As a connective it possesses the following truth table.

$p(x)$	$q(x)$	$p(x) \Rightarrow q(x)$
T	T	T
T	F	F
F	T	T
F	F	T

This defines "implies" precisely and we see that $p(x) \Rightarrow q(x)$ is only false, as a description of a situation, when $p(x)$ is true but $q(x)$ is false. How it is that $p(x) \Rightarrow q(x)$ can be true if $p(x)$ is false is often difficult to appreciate at first. However, consider the statement "if the communication cord is pulled the train will stop". We would regard this statement to be a true description of how the communication cord works if, indeed, the train did stop when the cord was pulled. This state of affairs corresponds to the first row in the truth table above. If the train did not stop when the cord was pulled we would regard the statement to be a false description, and this corresponds to the second row in the truth table. However, since a train can either stop (at a station, say) or not, as the case may be, when the cord is not pulled, then we accept that the description of how the communication cord works is still true in these cases. This illustrates why $p(x) \Rightarrow q(x)$ is true when $p(x)$ is false in the third and fourth rows of the truth table.

The equivalence connective

As well as the implication connective there is the equivalence or if-and-only-if connective. The expression "$p(x)$ is equivalent to $q(x)$" or "$p(x)$ if and only if $q(x)$" is written formally as

$$p(x) \Leftrightarrow q(x)$$

The equivalence connective is often called the double implication connective because its truth table is the same as that of the predicate

$$(p(x) \Rightarrow q(x)) \wedge (q(x) \Rightarrow p(x))$$

Its truth table is therefore as follows.

$p(x)$	$q(x)$	$p(x) \Leftrightarrow q(x)$
T	T	T
T	F	F
F	T	F
F	F	T

This connective is used to capture statements such as "$p(x)$ is true is equivalent to $q(x)$ is true". Thus, in defining the positive square root function we might well use the following defining predicate

$$y = \text{sqrt}(x) \Leftrightarrow (x \geqslant 0) \wedge (y \geqslant 0) \wedge (y * y = x)$$

where, again, the symbol * stands for multiplication. Armed with this new notation, we now consider various ways of giving function definitions.

Specifying functions

A function definition may be written in Z in the following way.

```
| function signature
|-------------------
| defining predicate
```

It is similar to a schema and provides a structured way of defining a function. Let us now consider the different ways in which the *input,output* pairs that make up a function can be specified.

Direct enumeration
Suppose we want to specify a function, called *dpm*, that will return the number of days in a given month during an ordinary (non-leap) year. On the assumption that *MONTH* has been defined we can write out a definition of *dpm* as follows.

$$dpm : MONTH \longrightarrow \mathbb{N}$$

$$dpm = \{(january,31),(february,28),(march,31),\\ (april,30),(may,31),(june,30),\\ (july,31),(august,31),(september,30),\\ (october,31),(november,30),(december,31)\}$$

All that we have done is list out the ordered pairs that make up *dpm*. An alternative to using ordered pairs is to make use of maplets. Using maplets the *dpm* function may be defined as follows.

$$dpm : MONTH \longrightarrow \mathbb{N}$$

$$dpm = \{january \mapsto 31,\ february \mapsto 28,\ march \mapsto 31,\\ april \mapsto 30,\ may \mapsto 31,\ june \mapsto 30,\\ july \mapsto 31,\ august \mapsto 31,\ september \mapsto 30,\\ october \mapsto 31,\ november \mapsto 30,\ december \mapsto 31\}$$

A function, therefore, can be regarded as a set of ordered pairs of the form (*input,output*) or equivalently as a set of maplets of the form $input \mapsto output$.

To signify that the pair (x,y), or equivalently the maplet $x \mapsto y$, belongs to the function f we write

$$(x,y) \in f \quad \text{or} \quad (x \mapsto y) \in f \quad \text{or} \quad y = f\ x$$

Explicit definition of the function rule
If the number of elements in the domain becomes large then specifying the function by direct enumeration can become tedious, and is impossible when the function contains an infinite number of maplets. On the other hand, if the rule by which function values can be obtained is known, then the function can be defined in a concise manner by specifying this rule explicitly. Thus to specify the function *sumsq*, that adds the squares of two real numbers together to form its output, we could specify the rule directly as follows.

$$
\begin{array}{|l}
sumsq : \mathbb{R} \times \mathbb{R} \longrightarrow \mathbb{R} \\
\hline
\forall\ x,y,z : \mathbb{R} \bullet \\
((x,y) \mapsto z) \in sumsq \Rightarrow z = x*x + y*y
\end{array}
$$

More succinctly we could write

$$
\begin{array}{|l}
sumsq : \mathbb{R} \times \mathbb{R} \longrightarrow \mathbb{R} \\
\hline
\forall\ x,y : \mathbb{R} \bullet \\
sumsq(x,y) = x*x + y*y
\end{array}
$$

Here it is imperative that the rule is specified directly because the number of elements in dom *sumsq* is infinite and it is impossible to list out all the maplets.

We could specify the days per month function more directly using the well known rule that begins "30 days hath September, April, June and November ...". If we define *ThirtyDays* as follows

$$ThirtyDays == \{september, april, june, november\}$$

then an alternative way of defining *dpm* would be

$$
\begin{array}{|l}
dpm : MONTH \longrightarrow \mathbb{N} \\
\hline
\forall\ m : MONTH \bullet \\
m \in ThirtyDays \Rightarrow dpm(m) = 30 \\
m \notin ThirtyDays \land m \neq february \Rightarrow dpm(m) = 31 \\
m = february \Rightarrow dpm(m) = 28
\end{array}
$$

Implicit definition of the function rule

Sometimes it is not convenient (or easy) to specify a function rule directly. We might not know how to do it, for example! However, if we know what a function has to do, rather than how it is to do it, then we can still give a formal, but implicit, definition of the function rule. Consider the positive square root button on a calculator. To specify directly how to obtain the square root of a number is quite complicated. However, we can specify the square root function in an implicit way as follows.

$$
\begin{array}{|l}
sqrt : \mathbb{R} \rightarrowtail\!\!\!\!\!+ \; \mathbb{R} \\
\hline
\text{dom } sqrt = \{x : \mathbb{R} \mid x \geq 0\} \\
\forall x,y : \mathbb{R} \mid x \geq 0 \bullet \\
(x \mapsto y) \in sqrt \Rightarrow y \geq 0 \wedge y*y = x
\end{array}
$$

An alternative and shorter definition using the equivalence connective is the following one.

$$
\begin{array}{|l}
sqrt : \mathbb{R} \rightarrowtail\!\!\!\!\!+ \; \mathbb{R} \\
\hline
\forall x,y : \mathbb{R} \bullet \\
y = sqrt\ x \Leftrightarrow x \geq 0 \wedge y \geq 0 \wedge y*y = x
\end{array}
$$

In both these definitions the properties that the function inputs and outputs must satisfy for the resulting pairs to belong to the function are declared. Nowhere do they include how $sqrt\ x$ is to be evaluated.

The set of partial functions $X \rightarrowtail\!\!\!\!\!+ \; Y$

When we first introduced the special notation that exists for the set of partial functions from X to Y, namely $X \rightarrowtail\!\!\!\!\!+ \; Y$, we did not have all the notation necessary to define the set. Now that we possess this notation it is useful to give a definition of what we mean by the set of partial functions from X to Y. The definition is the following.

$$
\begin{aligned}
X \rightarrowtail\!\!\!\!\!+ \; Y == \{f : \mathbb{P}(X \times Y) \mid (\forall x : X ; y_1,y_2 : Y \bullet \\
(x \mapsto y_1) \in f \wedge (x \mapsto y_2) \in f \Rightarrow y_1 = y_2)\}
\end{aligned}
$$

This reads as follows:

> "the set of partial functions from X to Y is defined to be the set of functions f from $\mathbb{P}(X \times Y)$, such that for all x in X and y_1, y_2 in Y, then the maplet $x \mapsto y_1$ belonging to f and the maplet $x \mapsto y_2$ belonging to f implies that $y_1 = y_2$".

Here the uniqueness property is being spelled out, together with the fact that a function from X to Y is an element from the power set of the Cartesian product $X \times Y$.

The set of total functions $X \longrightarrow Y$

The set of total functions from X to Y is relatively easy to define in terms of the set $X \rightarrowtail\!\!\!\!\!+ \; Y$ and its definition is as follows.

$$X \longrightarrow Y == \{f : X \rightarrowtail\!\!\!\!\!+ \; Y \mid \text{dom } f = X\}$$

The definition is simply stating the fact that total functions from X to Y are partial functions with their domains equal to the set X.

4.5 RECURSIVELY DEFINED FUNCTIONS

Having looked at the specification of the square root button on a calculator it is instructive to consider the definition of another function commonly found on calculators, the *factorial* function. This function is defined over the natural numbers and factorial n, written as $n!$, is given by the product

$$n! = n*(n-1)*(n-2)* \ldots *3*2*1$$

This function is used in applications requiring the number of ways in which various events can arise, and occurs in the study of computational complexity, for example. For our purposes, the function is important because it can be defined conveniently in a self-referencing, or recursive way.

Since $(n-1)!$ is $(n-1)*(n-2)* \ldots *3*2*1$, it follows that

$$n! = n*(n-1)!$$

Thus *factorial* n is the same as $n*factorial(n-1)$.

If we define $0!$ to be 1 then this, together with the recursive property, is sufficient to enable us to give a definition of the function. We specify the *factorial* function recursively as follows.

$$\begin{array}{|l} factorial : \mathbb{N} \longrightarrow \mathbb{N} \\ \hline factorial\ 0 = 1 \\ \forall n : \mathbb{N} \mid n > 0 \bullet \\ factorial\ n = n*factorial(n-1) \end{array}$$

To check that this definition does work, consider its use in working out $4!$. According to the definition we have that

$$\begin{aligned} 4! &= 4*3! \\ &= 4*3*2! \\ &= 4*3*2*1! \\ &= 4*3*2*1*0! \\ &= 4*3*2*1*1 \\ &= 24 \end{aligned}$$

which is the required result.

Recursion is a very powerful way of defining a function. As you progress through the book you will meet recursion in many guises, but in each application you will see that the object being specified – and it need not be a function – will possess an underlying structure that is inherently recursive. More examples of recursive functions are to be found in the worked examples considered next.

4.6 WORKED EXAMPLES

Example 1 : Partial functions in use

Our first example illustrates how partial functions may be used as convenient data structures within specifications.

- Give a specification of a simple telephone directory that allows up to 100 entries. Provision in the specification should be made to add a new entry, to remove an old entry, and to query the directory to obtain the telephone number of a person whose name is in the directory.

Solution

To capture the finite nature of our simple telephone directory we shall model it using a finite partial function, called *dir*, from an appropriate set of names to the set of natural numbers $\mathbb{N}$. We begin, therefore, by parachuting into the specification the basic type called *NAME* as follows.

$[NAME]$

Next we introduce the set of finite partial functions from *NAME* to $\mathbb{N}$, which in Z is written as follows

$NAME \twoheadrightarrow\!\!\!\!\!\!\!\shortmid\;\; \mathbb{N}$

and regard *dir* as an element from this set. This new arrow, for finite partial functions, allows us to use the cardinality operator to specify that *dir* should contain no more than 100 maplets.

The state of our directory, together with its initial state, can now be specified as follows.

```
┌─Directory──────────────────
│ dir : NAME -+» ℕ
├─────────────────
│ #dir ≤ 100
└────────────────────────────
```

```
┌─InitDirectory──────────────
│ Directory
├─────────────────
│ dir = { }
└────────────────────────────
```

The initial state schema thus sets up an empty directory with no entries in it.

We can add an entry to the directory via an *Add* operation whose specification is the following.

```
┌─Add──────────────────────────────
│ ΔDirectory
│ name? : NAME
│ number? : ℕ
├──────────────────────────
│ #dir < 100
│ name? ∉ dom dir
│ dir' = dir ∪ {name? ↦ number?}
└──────────────────────────────────
```

We cannot add to a full directory and hence the first precondition must apply. Also, to preserve the uniqueness property of the function *d*ir, we would not wish to add an existing *name*?,*number*? pair to the directory, which explains the second precondition. Finally the directory is updated using the set union operation which adds the new maplet to the function *dir*.

An existing entry is removed from the directory using the set difference operator. The *Remove* schema which specifies this operation is as follows.

```
┌─Remove───────────────────────────
│ ΔDirectory
│ name? : NAME
├──────────────────────────
│ name? ∈ dom dir
│ dir' = dir \ {name? ↦ dir name?}
└──────────────────────────────────
```

To query the directory, to obtain the telephone number of a person whose name is in the directory, we can use the following *QueryForNumber* operation.

```
┌─QueryForNumber───────────────────
│ ΞDirectory
│ name? : NAME
│ num! : ℕ
├──────────────────────────
│ name? ∈ dom dir
│ num! = dir name?
└──────────────────────────────────
```

Example 2 : Reasoning about function properties
This second example illustrates the power of formal reasoning to demonstrate the consistency of part of a specification.

- Show that the *Add* operation, as specified, preserves the data invariant in the *Directory* schema.

Solution
The data invariant is the single predicate $\#dir \leq 100$. In the *Add* schema the expression for the after state of *dir* is given by

$$dir' = dir \cup \{name? \mapsto number?\}$$

Thus it follows that

$$\#dir' = \#(dir \cup \{name? \mapsto number?\})$$

The right-hand side of this expression is equal to

$$\#dir + \#\{name? \mapsto number?\} - \#(dir \cap \{name? \mapsto number?\})$$

Since the precondition $name? \notin \mathrm{dom}\ dir$ applies to the *Add* operation, the set representing $dir \cap \{name? \mapsto number?\}$ will be empty. Thus

$$\#dir' = \#dir + 1 - 0$$

For the *Add* operation to work we see that $\#dir < 100$ has to be true, and therefore $\#dir + 1$ must be less than or equal to 100. It follows therefore that

$$\#dir' = \#dir + 1 \leq 100$$

The data invariant is thus preserved by the *Add* operation.

Example 3 : Investigating schema preconditions
This example demonstrates how systematic analysis of schema preconditions enables the error messages to be identified that are needed when robust user interfaces are being developed.

- Define a free type called *REPORT* that contains the appropriate error messages needed for *RAdd*, *RRemove* and *RQueryForNumber*.

Solution
The preconditions for the *Add* operation are

$$\#dir < 100 \quad \text{and} \quad name? \notin \mathrm{dom}\ dir$$

The only way in which $\#dir < 100$ can be violated is if $\#dir = 100$. In other words if the directory is full. A suitable error message in this case will be *directory_full*. If the precondition $name? \notin \text{dom } dir$ is violated, then *name?* must belong to dom *dir*. A suitable error message here is *name_in_directory*.

If we consider the *Remove* operation we see that its only precondition is $name? \in \text{dom } dir$. This is violated if $name? \notin \text{dom } dir$ applies. In other words the input *name?* is not in the domain of the directory function. A suitable message is therefore *name_not_known*.

The *QueryForNumber* schema has as its precondition the predicate $name? \in \text{dom } dir$, which is the same precondition as that for *Remove*. The same message, *name_not_known*, is also appropriate.

Remembering to include an appropriate message to indicate the successful operation of a schema we can define the free type *REPORT* as follows.

$$REPORT ::= ok \mid directory\_full \mid name\_in\_directory \mid name\_not\_known$$

Example 4 : defining functions

In this example we define two functions. The first is by direct enumeration and the second is via the use of recursion.

- (i) Specify a function that will check the value of a coin and return its value in pence as a natural number.

  (ii) Give a recursive definition of a function called *prod* that takes two natural numbers and returns their product as output.

Solution

(i) Assuming the existence of a basic type called *COIN* we can specify a function that returns the value of a coin in pence as follows.

$$value : COIN \rightarrowtail \mathbb{N}$$

$$value = \{1p \mapsto 1,\ 2p \mapsto 2,\ 5p \mapsto 5,\ 10p \mapsto 10,\ 20p \mapsto 20,\ 50p \mapsto 50,\ £1 \mapsto 100,\ £2 \mapsto 200\}$$

The basic assumption being made is that the *value* function, as specified here, has domain equal to the set of coins in sterling currency. The function does not accept any other coin and return its value in pence, for example.

(ii) The *prod* function can be defined recursively in terms of the usual + and − operators of ordinary arithmetic as follows.

$$\begin{array}{|l} prod : \mathbb{N} \times \mathbb{N} \longrightarrow \mathbb{N} \\ \hline \forall x,y : \mathbb{N} \bullet \\ y = 0 \Rightarrow prod(x,y) = 0 \\ y \neq 0 \Rightarrow prod(x,y) = x + prod(x,y-1) \end{array}$$

4.7 EXERCISES

1. Complete the specification of the telephone directory system by building the following robust operations: *RAdd*, *RRemove* and *RQueryForNumber*. The free type *REPORT* defined in worked example 3 should be used for the error reporting that is needed.

2. Show that the *Remove* operation preserves the data invariant given in the *Directory* schema.

3. Noting the fact that $x^n = x*x^{n-1}$, give a recursive definition of a function, called *power*, that will take a real number x and a natural number n as input and return, as output, the value of x raised to the power n.

4. The following is the state schema for a simple banking system where each account has a balance and an overdraft limit expressed in pence.

```
┌─Account──────────────────────────
│ balance, od_limit : ACC_NO ⇸ ℤ
├──────────────────────────────────
│ dom balance = dom od_limit
│ ∀ x : dom balance •
│ balance(x) ≥ od_limit(x)
│ od_limit(x) ≤ 0
└──────────────────────────────────
```

Deduce what the data invariant is saying and what changes would need to be made if overdraft limits were stored as positive (or zero) amounts and not as negative (or zero) amounts as indicated here.

CHAPTER 5

Functions in action

5.1 INTRODUCTION

In Chapter 4 we saw how functions could be defined and how they could be used as data models in system specifications. When state variables are modelled as functions, then operations that change the state of the system will change the functions involved. We have seen how operations such as set union and set difference can be used to alter functions. In this chapter we consider other ways in which functions can be modified.

We also look at functions that take other function values as their inputs and investigate the process known as function composition. We discuss the concept of an inverse function and continue our study of schema operations by looking briefly at schema composition.

5.2 RESTRICTING A FUNCTION

A convenient way of modifying a function is to restrict its operation in some way.

Domain restriction

One way of restricting the operation of a function is to restrict its domain. A telephone directory function, for example, may have been specified and we may wish to consider only those maplets whose domain element happens to belong to the set of names of people living in a particular zone. Or we may wish to consider only those maplets whose domain element belongs to the set of female names. In each case we are restricting the domain of the directory function to a given set.

A function $f : X \mapsto Y$ that has had its domain restricted to a set $A : \mathbb{P}\ X$ is written as follows.

$$A \lhd f$$

A formal definition of the restricted function $A \lhd f$ can be given using the set comprehension notation that we met in Section 3.4 of Chapter 3 as follows.

$$A \lhd f = \{x : X ; y : Y \mid x \in A \land (x \mapsto y) \in f \bullet x \mapsto y\}$$

Note that this definition does not necessarily mean that the set A is now the domain of $A \lhd f$. The domain of $A \lhd f$ is given as follows.

$$\mathrm{dom}(A \lhd f) = A \cap \mathrm{dom}(f)$$

As an example of domain restriction consider how the simple telephone directory system developed in Chapter 4 may be queried to furnish the set of telephone numbers of females who are in the directory. If *FEMALE_NAME* is the set containing the names of all females, then such a querying operation can be specified as follows.

```
┌─QueryForNumbers──────────────
│ ΞDirectory
│ numbers! : ℙ NAMES
├──────────────────────────
│ numbers! = ran(FEMALE_NAME ◁ dir)
└──────────────────────────────
```

Note how concisely the querying operation can be specified using domain restriction.

As a more indirect use of domain restriction, consider the following definition of the function *dpmleap*, which gives the days per month in a leap year.

```
│ dpmleap : MONTH → ℕ
├──────────────────────────
│ dpmleap = (MONTH \ {february}) ◁ dpm ∪
│                        {february ↦ 29}
```

Here, to create the new leap year function, we have restricted *dpm* to the set given by $MONTH \setminus \{february\}$, and added in the new maplet $february \mapsto 29$ using the set union operation. Again, it is worth noting how concisely we have been able to specify this new function.

Domain subtraction

Instead of restricting a function by specifying those elements that we would wish to see in the domain, it is sometimes more convenient to specify those that we do not wish to see. This can be done by domain anti-restriction or, as it is commonly called, domain subtraction.

Given the function $f : X \rightarrowtail\!\!\!\!\!+ \; Y$ and the set $B : \mathbb{P}\, X$ of elements that we do not wish to see in the domain, we write

$$B \ntriangleleft f$$

for the function that has had elements in B removed from its domain. Formally the function $B \ntriangleleft f$ can be defined as follows.

$$B \ntriangleleft f = \{x : X ; y : Y \mid x \in X \setminus B \land (x \mapsto y) \in f \bullet x \mapsto y\}$$

In other words $B \ntriangleleft f = (X \setminus B) \triangleleft f$.

As an example of domain subtraction consider the following alternative definition of the *dpmleap* function in terms of *dpm*.

$$dpmleap : MONTH \longrightarrow \mathbb{N}$$

$$dpmleap = (\{february\} \ntriangleleft dpm) \cup \{february \mapsto 29\}$$

This is a little more concise than the previous version. We have taken *february* out of the domain of *dpm* and then added in the new maplet $february \mapsto 29$ to create the required *dpmleap* function.

Range restriction and subtraction

There is nothing special about restricting the domain of a function. We could just as easily restrict the function by restricting its range. A function $f : X \nrightarrow Y$ that has been restricted so that elements in its range are also in the set $C : \mathbb{P}\ Y$, is written as

$$f \triangleright C$$

A function that has been restricted to ensure that elements in a set $D : \mathbb{P}\ Y$ are not in its range, is written

$$f \ntriangleright D$$

The first kind of restriction is known as range restriction; the second kind is known as range anti-restriction or range subtraction.

Formally the range-restricted function $f \triangleright C$ can be defined via the following set comprehension.

$$f \triangleright C = \{x : X ; y : Y \mid y \in C \land (x \mapsto y) \in f \bullet x \mapsto y\}$$

A definition of the range-subtracted function $f \ntriangleright D$, is therefore

$$f \ntriangleright D = \{x : X ; y : Y \mid y \in Y \setminus D \land (x \mapsto y) \in f \bullet x \mapsto y\}$$

Thus it follows that

$$f \ntriangleright D = f \triangleright (Y \setminus D)$$

As an example of range restriction in action, consider range restricting the *dpm* function to the set containing the number 31. In this way we can conveniently define the set of months that contain 31 days.

$$ThirtyOneDays : \mathbb{P}\ MONTH$$

$$ThirtyOneDays = \text{dom}(dpm \rhd \{31\})$$

This same set could also be defined using range subtraction as follows.

$$ThirtyOneDays : \mathbb{P}\ MONTH$$

$$ThirtyOneDays = \text{dom}(dpm \mathbin{\rhd\!\!\!-} \{28,\ 30\})$$

More illustrations using domain and range restriction and subtraction can be found in the worked examples section of this chapter, where their particular use in schemas is considered.

5.3 OVERRIDING A FUNCTION

Very often we need to modify a function by adding new maplets and changing those already in the function. For example, let the following set of maplets be the function that specifies the current room numbers of staff in offices on the third floor of a building.

$$\{allan \mapsto 313,\ mike \mapsto 310,\ glinn \mapsto 311,\ hugh \mapsto 311,\ ray \mapsto 314,\ jeff \mapsto 314,\ david \mapsto 310,\ maggie \mapsto 316,\ john \mapsto 315,\ patricia \mapsto 316\}$$

Suppose a new member of staff arrives, whose name is *anthony*, and he is put in room 312. Suppose, too, that *allan* moves out of his office into room 316. If we model the original allocation of staff to rooms by a function called f, then these updates can be made in a single override operation, written as follows.

$$f \oplus \{anthony \mapsto 312,\ allan \mapsto 316\}$$

The maplet $allan \mapsto 313$ in the original function f is overridden by the new maplet $allan \mapsto 316$ and the maplet $anthony \mapsto 312$ is added to f.

In general, given two functions g and h, each of the form $X \mathbin{+\!\!\!\rightarrow} Y$, we define g overriden by h, which is written $g \oplus h$, as follows.

$$g \oplus h = (\text{dom}(h) \mathbin{\lhd\!\!\!-} g) \cup h$$

Thus, to override g by h we domain restrict g to the set of elements that are not in the domain of h, and add in those maplets in h by use of the set union operation.

Function override is used extensively in specifications to update functions. The operation always results in a set of maplets that is, itself, a function. It is worth noting that updating a function by the operation of set union cannot, for example, guarantee to preserve the uniqueness property of the resulting set of maplets. Note, too, that the override operation enables us to specify function updates very concisely. For example, the *dpmleap* function can be defined succinctly in terms of *dpm* as follows.

$$dpmleap : MONTH \longrightarrow \mathbb{N}$$

$$dpmleap = dpm \oplus \{february \mapsto 29\}$$

Also, with reference to the telephone directory system that was specified in Chapter 4, we can define an operation to change a user's telephone number as follows.

ChangeNumber

$\Delta Directory$
$name? : NAME$
$newnum? : \mathbb{N}$

$name? \in \mathrm{dom}\ dir$
$dir' = dir \oplus \{name? \mapsto newnum?\}$

5.4 FUNCTION COMPOSITION

Being able to build new objects from objects already defined is as fundamental to software engineering as it is to any other engineering discipline. In previous chapters sets were built from sets, types constructed out of types, and schemas written in terms of schemas. With function override two functions were combined to give a new function. One of the most powerful ways of building functions from functions is to use function composition.

Suppose a function, called *office*, returns a room number when supplied with an employee's name. Suppose the function called *phone* takes a room number and returns the number of the telephone in that room. If we need to specify an office telephone directory, this can be done conveniently in terms of *office* and *phone* by using function composition. In function composition the output from the first function is used as the input to the second function. Thus composing *office* and *phone*, and supplying the composite function with an employee's name, means that *office* furnishes the room number which is then used by *phone* to give the required telephone number of the employee. The office telephone directory function can be written in terms of the functions *office* and *phone* as follows

$$phone \circ office$$

and is the notation that stands for *office* composed with *phone*.

In general, if g and h are two functions from X to Y and from Y to Z respectively, then the set of maplets in $h \circ g$ will be a function from X to Z that can be defined as follows.

$$h \circ g = \{x : X ; y : Y ; z : Z \mid (x \mapsto y) \in g \land (y \mapsto z) \in h \bullet x \mapsto z\}$$

This definition of $h \circ g$ does not imply that the domain of $h \circ g$ will necessarily be the same as the domain of g. In our office telephone directory it could be that certain employees, who have a room, do not in fact possess a telephone number because their room is without a telephone. In general it is the case that

$$\text{dom}(h \circ g) \subseteq \text{dom } g$$

and only if ran $g \subseteq$ dom h will it be that $\text{dom}(h \circ g) = \text{dom } g$.

Having defined function composition it is important to remember that the notation $h \circ g$ means first apply g and follow it by h. If x, for example, is an element in the domain of $h \circ g$ then the action of $h \circ g$ on x is often written as

$$h(g(x))$$

Thus, taking function names to have their obvious meaning, it follows that

$$square \circ sum(6,3) =$$
$$square(sum(6,3)) = square(9) = 81$$

Where it is appropriate, functions can be composed with themselves and with other functions any number of times. In this way an impressive array of functions can be built up from only a few simple basic ones. This, of course, is the way in which functional programming languages such as LISP or ML operate.

An alternative to writing $h \circ g$, that better signifies the order in which functions operate in function composition, is to use the "fat semi colon" notation. If we write

$$g \, ⨟ \, h$$

then this is exactly the same as the composed function $h \circ g$.

5.5 THE INVERSE OF A FUNCTION AND INVERSE FUNCTIONS

The inverse of a function $f : X \nrightarrow Y$, written as $f^{\sim}$, is defined in Z in the following way.

$$f^{\sim} = \{x : X ; y : Y \mid (x \mapsto y) \in f \bullet y \mapsto x\}$$

In other words it is the set consisting of the maplets of f, but written in reverse order. All functions, therefore, have inverses as defined here, but the set of maplets making up $f^{\sim}$ need not necessarily represent a function. When a set represents a function we say that $f^{\sim}$ is the inverse function of f, as opposed to simply being the inverse of f.

The inverse function of a function f from X to Y can be defined formally as follows.

$$\begin{aligned} f^{\sim} = \{x : X ; y : Y \mid (x \mapsto y) \in f \wedge \\ (\forall x_1, x_2 : \mathrm{dom}\ f \bullet (f\ x_1 = f\ x_2) \Rightarrow (x_1 = x_2)) \bullet y \mapsto x\} \end{aligned}$$

Note that the predicate given by

$$\forall x_1, x_2 : \mathrm{dom}\ f \bullet (f\ x_1 = f\ x_2) \Rightarrow (x_1 = x_2)$$

ensures that $f^{\sim}$ has the uniqueness property that all functions must possess. The uniqueness property is now preserved both ways, in going from X to Y under f, but also in going from Y back to X under $f^{\sim}$. Let us consider a specific example of an inverse and an inverse function.

Let us return to the set of maplets that we considered when we were discussing function override in Section 5.3, namely

$$\begin{aligned} \{&allan \mapsto 313, mike \mapsto 310, glinn \mapsto 311, hugh \mapsto 311, \\ &ray \mapsto 314, jeff \mapsto 314, david \mapsto 310, maggie \mapsto 316, \\ &john \mapsto 315, patricia \mapsto 316\} \end{aligned}$$

This set makes up the function that we called f. If we think of f as being the set of maplets of the form $x \mapsto y$, then the set of maplets of the form $y \mapsto x$ is

$$\begin{aligned} \{&313 \mapsto allan, 310 \mapsto mike, 311 \mapsto glinn, 311 \mapsto hugh, \\ &314 \mapsto ray, 314 \mapsto jeff, 310 \mapsto david, 316 \mapsto maggie, \\ &315 \mapsto john, 316 \mapsto patricia\} \end{aligned}$$

This set of maplets, which is the inverse of f, is most certainly not a function because it is not clear at all to which person room number 310 corresponds, and the same is true for room numbers 311, 314 and 316. If we compare this set with our definition of an inverse function, then the predicate that ensures that $f^{\sim}$ will possess the required uniqueness property is clearly not satisfied. We note, for example, that $f(mike) = f(david)$, but that $mike \neq david$. Thus our given set of maplets does not possess an inverse which is a function.

However, we can construct a meaningful inverse function to tell us who is in a particular office by restricting the original set of maplets. If we domain restrict our original set f to the set

$$\{allan, mike, glinn, ray, maggie, john\}$$

then the restricted set of maplets is now

$$\{allan \mapsto 313, mike \mapsto 310, glinn \mapsto 311, ray \mapsto 314, maggie \mapsto 316, john \mapsto 315\}$$

Its inverse, obtained by reversing the maplets, is the following.

$$\{313 \mapsto allan, 310 \mapsto mike, 311 \mapsto glinn, 314 \mapsto ray, 316 \mapsto maggie, 315 \mapsto john\}$$

This is a perfectly respectable function, possessing the uniqueness property that is required, and it can be used to tell us who is in a particular office. In general, by the appropriate use of domain restriction, it is usually possible to construct a suitable inverse function for any given function.

5.6 SCHEMA COMPOSITION

Just as functions can be thought of as generating outputs from inputs, operations that change the state of a system can be thought of as generating final states from initial states. By analogy with function composition, where we allow outputs from one function to become inputs to another, we can allow final states of one schema to become the initial states of another by a process known as schema composition.

If the final states of a schema S are to become the initial states of a schema T then we write the composite operation as

$$S \fatsemi T$$

To appreciate how schema composition works, we need to know how to hide variables within a schema.

Schema hiding

Consider the following subtract schema.

```
┌─Subtract──────────────────────────────────────
│ first no?, second no?, result! : ℕ
├───────────────────────────
│ first no? > second no?
│ first no? = second no? + result!
└───────────────────────────────────────────────
```

This is exactly the same, in its effect, as the schema

```
┌─NewSubtract───────────────────────────────────
│ first no?, second no? : ℕ
├───────────────────────────
│ first no? > second no?
│ ∃ result! : ℕ • first? = second? + result!
└───────────────────────────────────────────────
```

The only difference is that the variable *result*! has been removed from the signature of the first schema and introduced into the predicate of the second schema via an existential quantifier. In the second schema we say that the variable *result*! has been hidden. There is nothing special about the fact that an output variable has been hidden and any variable, be it a state variable, an input or an output, can be hidden in this way.

There is a standard way of writing a schema in which some of its variables have been hidden. If a schema S has had variables x_1, x_2, ..., x_n hidden, then the resulting schema is written as follows.

$$S \setminus (x_1, x_2, \ldots, x_n)$$

Thus in the subtraction example above the schema called *NewSubtract*, with the variable *result*! hidden, can be expressed in terms of the schema *Subtract* as follows.

NewSubtract ≙ *Subtract* \ (*result*!)

Let us now see how the hiding of variables is used in schema composition.

Schema composition

For the schema $S \mathbin{;} T$ to be defined, the final states of S have to match the initial states of T, in the sense that S has a variable x' if and only if T has a variable x, and their types are the same. To obtain the schema $S \mathbin{;} T$ from S and T we first form the schema $S \wedge T$ by the usual process of schema conjunction. Next we hide the common final states of S and initial states of T using existential quantification in the predicates part of the conjoined schemas. The result is $S \mathbin{;} T$.

As an example let the first schema, S, be one called *AddTo* which enables an input $x?$ to be added to a state variable *total* as shown

```
┌─AddTo──────────────────────────
│ total, total', x? : ℕ
├────────────────────────
│ total' = total + x?
└────────────────────────────────
```

and let the second schema, T, be one called *TakeFrom* which enables an input $y?$ to be subtracted from the same state variable *total* as shown.

```
┌─TakeFrom───────────────────────
│ total, total', y? : ℕ
├────────────────────────
│ total ≥ y?
│ total' = total - y?
└────────────────────────────────
```

The composed schema *AddTo* ⨾ *TakeFrom*, which we might choose to call *AddThenTake*, is then the following schema, where the after state of *AddTo* and the before state of *TakeFrom* have each been called $total_0$ and hidden in the predicate.

```
┌─AddThenTake────────────────────
│ total, total', x?, y? : ℕ
├────────────────────────
│ ∃ total₀ : ℕ •
│ total₀ = total + x?
│ total₀ ≥ y?
│ total' = total₀ - y?
└────────────────────────────────
```

Obviously, some simplification is possible in the predicates part, and the *AddThenTake* schema can be rewritten as follows.

```
┌─AddThenTake────────────────────
│ total, total', x?, y? : ℕ
├────────────────────────
│ total + x? ≥ y?
│ total' = total + x? - y?
└────────────────────────────────
```

Examples illustrating schema composition are given in the next section.

5.7 WORKED EXAMPLES

Example 1 : Function operations in action
This first example shows how the function override operation may be used in the specification of a simple banking system along with other updating operations such as set union and set difference.

- Develop the specification of a simple banking system that will enable users of the bank to make deposits and withdrawals, allow new customers to open an account at the bank, and existing users to close down their accounts. Each account is to have a balance and an overdraft limit associated with it.

Solution
The basic types that will be needed in the specification are types to model account numbers and amounts of money. The following basic types are thus parachuted into the specification.

$$[ACC\_NO, \mathbb{Z}]$$

The set $\mathbb{Z}$ will be used to model amounts of money in pence, so that £498.53 is represented by the integer value 49853, for example.

The system state schema, which we shall call *Account*, can be written down in terms of two partial functions as follows.

```
┌─Account──────────────────────────
│ balance, od_limit : ACC_NO ⇸ ℤ
├──────────────────────
│ dom balance = dom od_limit
│ ∀ x : dom balance •
│ balance x ≥ od_limit x
│ od_limit x ≤ 0
└──────────────────────────────────
```

The partial function, *balance*, tells us the current balance associated with a particular account number, and the partial function, *od_limit*, supplies information on the overdraft limit associated with an account number. The predicate requires that each account has a balance and overdraft limit, and that the overdraft limit should not be exceeded. Note that overdraft limits are expressed as negative, or zero, amounts.

A valid initial state of the banking system is the following, which corresponds to a bank with no accounts.

```
┌─InitAccount──────────────────────
│ Account
├──────────────────────
│ balance = { }
│ od_limit = { }
└──────────────────────────────────
```

The operation that allows a new customer to open an account is the following.

```
┌─Open──────────────────────────────────────────
│ ΔAccount
│ new? : ACC_NO
│ odl? : ℤ
├──────────────────────────
│ new? ∉ dom balance
│ odl? ≥ 0
│ balance' = balance ∪ {new? ↦ 0}
│ od_limit' = od_limit ∪ {new? ↦ -odl?}
└───────────────────────────────────────────────
```

The predicate tests that *new?* is not already an existing account number and requires that *odl?* is non-negative. The balance associated with the new account number is set to zero, and the associated overdraft limit is set up with the value *-odl?*.

Operations for making a deposit and a withdrawal are specified conveniently by means of the function override operation. The predicates in each case test that the account holder is known to the bank and override the *balance* and *od_limit* functions accordingly.

```
┌─Deposit───────────────────────────────────────
│ ΔAccount
│ user_no? : ACC_NO
│ amount? : ℤ
├──────────────────────────
│ user_no? ∈ dom balance
│ amount? > 0
│ balance' = balance ⊕ {user_no? ↦
│              balance(user_no?) + amount?}
│ od_limit' = od_limit
└───────────────────────────────────────────────
```

```
┌─Withdraw──────────────────────────────────────
│ ΔAccount
│ user_no? : ACC_NO
│ amount? : ℤ
├──────────────────────────
│ user_no? ∈ dom balance
│ amount? > 0
│ balance(user_no?) - amount? ≥ od_limit(user_no?)
│ balance' = balance ⊕ {user_no? ↦
│              balance(user_no?) - amount?}
│ od_limit' = od_limit
└───────────────────────────────────────────────
```

Finally, the schema to specify how an account is closed down may be written as follows. The assumption is that an account can only be closed down after the balance is reduced (or made up to) zero.

```
┌─Close──────────────────────────────
│ ΔAccount
│ user_no? : ACC_NO
├──────────────────
│ user_no? ∈ dom balance
│ balance user_no? = 0
│ balance' = balance \ {user_no? ↦ 0}
│ od_limit' = od_limit \ {user_no? ↦
│             od_limit user_no?}
└────────────────────────────────────
```

Example 2 : Restricting a function
This example demonstrates how a system can be queried selectively by the use of range restriction.

- Write a querying operation to report the accounts with balances below a certain given amount.

Solution
If the given amount is an input to the querying operation, then an appropriate *QueryForAccounts* operation can be specified as follows

```
┌─QueryForAccounts───────────────────
│ ΞAccount
│ amount? : ℤ
│ accounts! : ℙ ACC_NO
├──────────────────
│ accounts! = dom(balance ▷ {x : ℤ | x < amount?})
└────────────────────────────────────
```

There is no precondition required because a possible output could well be the empty set of account numbers.

Example 3 : Schema composition
This example investigates the properties of a schema composition operation.

- Show formally that if a new user of the bank opens an account and then promptly closes down the account, the system state is unaltered.

Solution

The operation of opening an account and then closing down an account can be represented by the operation *Open* ⨾ *Close*. As a schema *Open* ⨾ *Close*, when expressed in full, has the following declarations and predicates

```
┌─Open⨾Close──────────────────────────────────
│ ΔAccount
│ new?, user_no? : ACC_NO
│ odl? : ℤ
├──────────────────────────
│ new? ∉ dom balance
│ odl? ≥ 0
│ ∃ balance₀, od_limit₀ : ACC_NO ⇸ ℤ •
│ balance₀ = balance ∪ {new? ↦ 0}
│ od_limit₀ = od_limit ∪ {new? ↦ -odl?}
│ user_no? ∈ dom balance₀
│ balance₀ user_no? = 0
│ balance' = balance₀ \ {user_no? ↦ 0}
│ od_limit' = od_limit₀ \ {user_no? ↦
│             od_limit₀ user_no?}
└─────────────────────────────────────────────
```

To show that *Open* ⨾ *Close* leaves the system state unaltered when *new?* and *user_no?* are the same account number then we must prove that *balance'* = *balance* and that *od_limit'* = *od_limit*.

From the predicates of *Open* ⨾ *Close* we see that

$$balance' = balance_0 \setminus \{user\_no? \mapsto 0\}$$

Since $balance_0 = balance \cup \{new? \mapsto 0\}$, then it follows that

$$balance' = (balance \cup \{new? \mapsto 0\} \setminus \{user\_no? \mapsto 0\}$$

Now, since $new? \notin \mathrm{dom}\ balance$, then the maplet $new? \mapsto 0$ will be an additional maplet to those already in balance. Thus when $user\_no? \mapsto 0$ is subsequently removed from $balance \cup \{new? \mapsto 0\}$, in the case when *new?* and *user_no?* are the same account number, the result will just be the set of maplets that originally made up *balance*. Thus it follows that

$$balance' = balance$$

If we now consider the function *od_limit'* it follows from the predicates of *Open* ⨾ *Close* that

$$od\_limit' = od\_limit_0 \setminus \{user\_no? \mapsto od\_limit_0\ user\_no?\}$$

Given that *new?* and *user_no?* are the same account number, we can write the expression for *od_limit'* as

$$od\_limit' = od\_limit_0 \setminus \{new? \mapsto od\_limit_0\ new?\}$$

Given that $od\_limit_0 = od\_limit \cup \{new? \mapsto -odl?\}$ it follows that

$$od\_limit' = (od\_limit \cup \{new? \mapsto -odl?\}) \setminus \{new? \mapsto -odl?\}$$

By the same argument that was used for the *balance* function, it follows that $(od\_limit \cup \{new? \mapsto -odl?\}) \setminus \{new? \mapsto -odl?\}$ is just the same as *od_limit*. Thus

$$od\_limit' = od\_limit$$

The composition of the two operations *Open* and *Close* does, indeed, leave the system state unchanged.

5.8 EXERCISES

1. Produce robust user interfaces for all the operations specified in the simple banking system.

2. Write a robust operation to allow users to change their overdraft limit in the context of the simple banking system.

3. Using domain subtraction specify a querying operation to allow the accounts of students to be identified and the set of balances and overdraft limits output. The set $StudentNumbers : \mathbb{P}\ ACC\_NO$ can be assumed to be known.

4. Verify that a user making a deposit of *x?*, and following this with a withdrawal from the bank of the same amount, leaves the system state variables unchanged.

CHAPTER 6

A real problem from start to finish : specifying the operation of a drinks machine

6.1 INTRODUCTION

So far the mathematical notation we have developed has only been used to specify relatively simple systems, or to give relatively straightforward definitions. In this chapter we use the notation to specify a more complicated system; the specification we build is that of software which simulates the operation of a typical drinks machine. The type of machine we have in mind is the one shown in figure 6.1, which enables users to select a variety of hot or cold drinks.

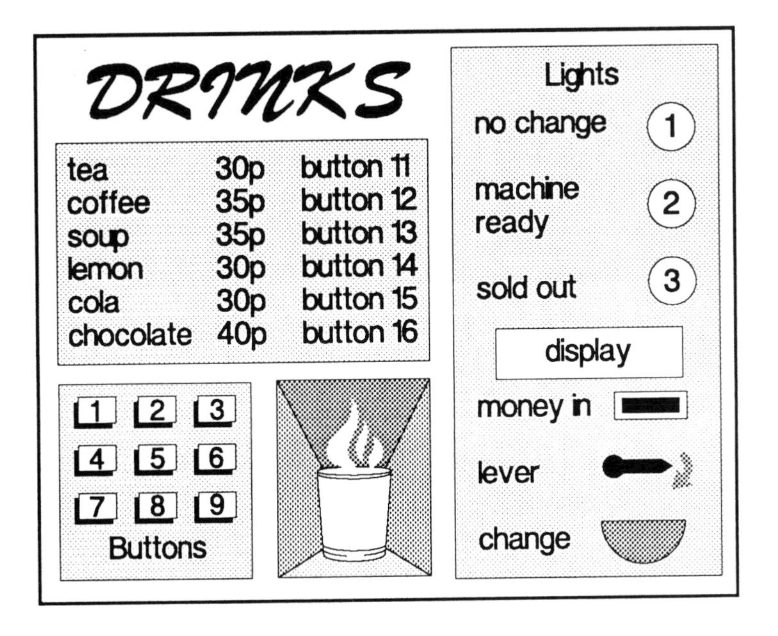

Figure 6.1 : A typical drinks machine

With its large selection of drinks, its array of warning lights, its cash display and its money back facility, the operation of the machine is relatively complicated. However, most people have used a vending machine, so there should be no problem coming to grips with this complexity. We therefore concentrate on the more important modelling and specification issues, without needing to worry about the intricacies of the problem domain. Our aim is to show that the ideas developed so far are just as appropriate for complex systems as they are for the simple systems we have considered.

We start with a discussion of how the machine works, so that the requirements of our system can be established.

6.2 ASSUMPTIONS ABOUT THE MACHINE'S OPERATION

We assume that the machine only functions if the "machine ready" light is lit and only delivers a drink if the "sold out" light is not on after selecting a drink. Should the "sold out" light come on, then money can be retrieved by pressing the appropriate money-back lever.

Money put into the machine, before any buttons are pressed, can also be retrieved by pressing this lever. Pressing the lever will cause the display to return to zero. Having put in enough money, and having pressed the appropriate buttons, a drink will be delivered, along with the correct change, provided the machine is not out of change. If the "no change" light is lit, then the assumption is that any change due will not in fact be given, but a drink will be supplied. Should the "sold out" light come on after selection then the lever can be used to return cash, in full, even if the "no change" light is lit.

As well as these assumptions, the machine has the ability to differentiate between the various coins that are put into it. It will not, for example, accept foreign currency or metal washers! We will assume, too, that money put in, if acceptable, is stored in a temporary input store until the drink is delivered. On delivery the money passes to a strong box housed inside the machine. If the money-back lever is used, it is the money in this temporary store that is returned to the user. Change that is given along with a drink is supplied from a central change-giving facility, which cannot be invoked by pressing the lever. There are other assumptions that will be needed as the specification progresses. These will be supplied when they are needed.

6.3 MODELLING THE STATE OF THE MACHINE

The state of the machine will involve a description of the cash display, information about the buttons to press to obtain a given drink, information about costs, a description of the warning lights and a description of the internal state of the machine.

To provide this description we need several basic types. First of all we parachute into our specification some rather obvious types as follows.

$[DRINK, COIN]$

As well as these we need a free type called *ON_OFF* that can be defined as follows.

$ON\_OFF ::= on \mid off$

Finally, we need to use the set of natural numbers, $\mathbb{N}$, to keep a record of the number of drinks sold and to account for the amount of money put into the machine.

In terms of these types and sets we can now give a structured description of the state of the machine. We do this firstly by specifying parts of the machine and assembling these parts later by use of the schema calculus.

The cash display

We model the state of the cash display by a natural number called *display*. When the machine is not in use the value of *display* is typically zero. We declare *display* to be a natural number in the following *Display* schema.

```
┌─Display──────────────────────
│ display : ℕ
└──────────────────────────────
```

Drinks information

The information about the buttons to press to obtain a drink, together with the costs of the drinks, is modelled by two partial functions as follows.

```
┌─Information──────────────────
│ drink : ℕ ⇸ DRINK
│ price : ℕ ⇸ ℕ
├──────────────────────
│ dom drink = dom price
└──────────────────────────────
```

If the sequence of buttons pressed to obtain a drink generates a natural number that belongs to the domain of *drink*, then the drink dispensed is that specified by the *drink* function. The associated price of the drink is the value in pence returned by the *price* function. The predicate of the *Information* schema ensures that the two partial functions, *drink* and *price*, relate to the same set of drinks.

The warning lights

The state of the warning lights on the machine is modelled by a partial function called *light* in a schema called *Lights* as follows.

```
┌─Lights──────────────────────────
│ light : ℕ ⇸ ON_OFF
└─────────────────────────────────
```

The lights on the machine have a unique identifying number in the domain of the function *light* and their state is either *on* or *off*. The function representing the state of the lights on the drinks machine shown in figure 6.1 will have a domain containing the natural numbers 1, 2 and 3. Light number 1 is the "no change" light, light number 2 is the "machine ready" light, and light number 3 is the "sold out" light.

The internal state of the machine

The internal state of the machine is modelled by two schemas called *InternalState* and *MoneyStore*. The *InternalState* schema keeps account of the number of drinks that remain in the machine and the amount of change that is left. This schema is specified as follows.

```
┌─InternalState───────────────────
│ drinksleft : DRINK ⇸ ℕ
│ changeleft : ℕ
└─────────────────────────────────
```

The *drinksleft* function simply returns the number of each drink remaining at any time, and *changeleft* represents the value, in pence, of the amount of change currently in the machine.

The *MoneyStore* schema is as follows.

```
┌─MoneyStore──────────────────────
│ input : COIN ⇸ ℕ
│ store : COIN ⇸ ℕ
├─────────────────────────
│ dom input = {1p, 2p, 5p, 10p, 20p, 50p}
│ dom input = dom store
└─────────────────────────────────
```

In this schema the function *input* keeps a record of the number of each coin in its domain that has been inserted into the machine's temporary store. The *store* function does the same for the money held in the strong box. The predicate of the *MoneyStore* schema states that the domain of *input* is the set containing 1p, 2p, 5p, 10p, 20p and 50p. These coins, therefore, are the only coins which the machine recognises.

The state schema

The state schema representing the state of the machine includes all the schemas we have written so far, and can be written as follows.

```
┌─Machine──────────────────────
│ Display
│ Information
│ Lights
│ InternalState
│ MoneyStore
├──────────────────
│ light 2 = on
│ ran drink = dom drinksleft
└──────────────────────────────
```

The predicate indicates that the value of *light* 2 is *on*. Thus the "machine ready" light has to be lit. In fact the specification we give only simulates the operation of a machine that is ready to be used. We do not attempt to specify what happens, for example, when the "machine ready" light goes out, or is not lit. The predicate that equates the range of *drink* to the domain of *drinksleft* is needed to ensure that *drink* and *drinksleft* relate to the same set of drinks in our machine.

The initial state

The initial state of the machine can be set up via the following *InitMachine* schema.

```
┌─InitMachine──────────────────────────────
│ Machine
├──────────────────────────
│ display = 0
│ drink = {11 ↦ tea, 12 ↦ coffee, 13 ↦ soup,
│          14 ↦ lemon, 15 ↦ cola, 16 ↦ choc}
│ price = {11 ↦ 30, 12 ↦ 35, 13 ↦ 35,
│          14 ↦ 30, 15 ↦ 30, 16 ↦ 40}
│ light = {1 ↦ off, 2 ↦ on, 3 ↦ off}
│ drinksleft = {tea ↦ 50, coffee ↦ 50, soup ↦ 50,
│               lemon ↦ 50, cola ↦ 50, choc ↦ 50}
│ changeleft = 1500
│ input = {1p ↦ 0, 2p ↦ 0, 5p ↦ 0,
│          10p ↦ 0, 20p ↦ 0, 50p ↦ 0}
│ store = {1p ↦ 0, 2p ↦ 0, 5p ↦ 0,
│          10p ↦ 0, 20p ↦ 0, 50p ↦ 0}
└──────────────────────────────────────────
```

The schema represents a machine full of drinks that is ready for use. There are 50 of each of the six drinks available, the machine can give out a total of £15 in change, the machine's strong box is empty and ready to receive money that will be put into the machine. It will be seen that the predicates in the state schema are satisfied by such an initialisation.

6.4 UTILITY FUNCTIONS

Before moving on to specify operations such as inserting a coin into the machine and the act of obtaining a drink, we need to specify two utility functions that will be needed in various operation schemas.

The first is a function called *value* that enables the machine to distinguish between the coins put into it and to supply the value of a coin in pence. Such a function can be defined as follows.

$$value : COIN \mathrel{+\!\!\!\rightarrow} \mathbb{N}$$

$$value = \{1p \mapsto 1,\ 2p \mapsto 2,\ 5p \mapsto 5,\ 10p \mapsto 10,\ 20p \mapsto 20,\ 50p \mapsto 50\}$$

The domain of *value* represents the set of coins that the machine recognises. Thus the *value* function only recognises 1p, 2p, 5p, 10p, 20p and 50p coins. A £1 coin cannot, for example, be inserted into the machine.

The second function that is needed is a *change* function that supplies change in 1p coins up to the value of the natural number that is input. Such a *change* function can be specified as a total function as follows.

$$change : \mathbb{N} \longrightarrow (COIN \mathrel{+\!\!\!\rightarrow} \mathbb{N})$$

$$change\ 0 = \{\}$$
$$\forall n : \mathbb{N} \mid n > 0 \bullet$$
$$change\ n = \{1p \mapsto n\}$$

The *change* function, when some change is needed, thus returns a set containing a maplet whose domain element is the 1p coin and whose range element corresponds to the number of coins needed to make up the change value required. For simplicity the function returns the empty set for a change value of zero.

A more sophisticated change function could be specified involving other coins in the change besides 1p. This is a relatively easy thing to do, but to keep things simple we will work with the change function that we have just specified.

6.5 MACHINE OPERATIONS

There are three operations that the user can initiate. These are inserting a coin into the machine, selecting a drink, and using the money-back lever when this proves necessary. We consider each of these operations in turn, starting with the operation of feeding a coin into the machine.

Inserting a coin into the machine
The schema that represents the simple act of inserting a coin into the machine can be written as follows.

```
┌─CoinIn──────────────────────────────
│ ΔMachine
│ ΞInformation
│ ΞLights
│ ΞInternal State
│ coin? : COIN
├──────────────────────────
│ coin? ∈ dom value
│ display' = display + value coin?
│ input = input ⊕ {coin? ↦ (input coin? + 1)}
│ store' = store
└─────────────────────────────────────
```

The signature is telling us that the state variables in the *Machine* schema are likely to change as a result of the operation being performed, but that the variables in *Information*, *Lights* and *InternalState* are definitely not changing. The only input to the operation is *coin*? of type *COIN*.

The predicate requires that *coin*? belongs to the domain of the function, *value* – in other words that *coin*? is a valid coin. The value of *display* is increased by the value of the coin that is inserted, and the number of coins equal to *coin*?, in the input store, is increased by 1. The value of *store* is unaltered because only if a drink is subsequently delivered will the contents of *input* be added to those of *store*.

Obtaining a drink with change
If a customer has put in sufficient money, pressed the appropriate buttons for a drink, and both the "sold out" and "no change" lights on the front of the machine remain unlit, it is reasonable to expect that the customer will receive a drink together with the appropriate amount of change. The *SuccessfulDrink* schema, given below, models the process whereby the drink, together with the full amount of change, are delivered. Notice that the schema does not preclude the act of keying in a request for a different drink should the "sold out" light have come on after keying in the first request.

The signature of the schema indicates that all the state variables apart from those in the *Information* schema are possibly going to change as a result of the operation. The only input to the operation is the button value *b*? and the outputs are the drink, *dr*!, and change, *ch*!.

```
—SuccessfulDrink————————————————————————
| ΔMachine
| ΞInformation
| b? : ℕ
| dr! : DRINK
| ch! : COIN ⇸ ℕ
|————————————————————————
| light 1 = off
| b? ∈ dom drink
| display ≥ price b?
| drinksleft(drink b?) > 0
| changeleft ≥ display - price b?
|
| dr! = drink b?
| ch! = change(display - price b?)
|
| display' = 0
| light' = light ⊕ {3 ↦ off}
| changeleft' = changeleft - (display - price b?)
| drinksleft' = drinksleft ⊕ {drink(b?) ↦
|                    drinksleft(drink b?) - 1}
| input' = {c : dom input • c ↦ 0}
| store' = {c : dom input • c ↦ (store c + input c)}
————————————————————————————————
```

For *SuccessfulDrink* to work the "no change" light has to be unlit and there should be sufficient change left to cover the difference between *display* and *price b*?. Obviously the button value *b*? should belong to the domain of the *drink* function, and the *display* value should not be less than the price of the drink being requested. We also require that *drinksleft*(*drink b*?) > 0 to ensure that the machine is able to supply the drink requested.

The outputs *dr*! and *ch*! are supplied in the obvious way and the state of the machine is updated appropriately. The display is returned to zero and light number 3, should it have been lit, is switched to its unlit state. The amount of change that is left is reduced by the change given. The quantity of the drink dispensed that remains is one less than the initial value of *drinksleft*(*drink b*?). Finally, the money in the machine's temporary store is all added to the money in the strong box, and every maplet in *input*' has its range element set to zero.

The money-back lever

Having put money into the machine users may, for whatever reason, decide not to go ahead with obtaining a drink. They may choose to retrieve the money put in by using the money-back lever. On the other hand, they may have put money into the machine, pressed the appropriate buttons for a drink, but the "sold out" light has come on.

The *MoneyBack* schema specifies the changes that occur to the state of the machine when money that has been put in is refunded.

```
┌─Moneyback──────────────────────────
│ Δmachine
│ ΞInformation
│ ΞInternalState
│ refund! : COIN ⇸ ℕ
├────────────────────────────
│ refund! = input
│ display' = 0
│ light' = light ⊕ {3 ↦ off}
│ input' = {c : dom input • c ↦ 0}
│ store' = store
└────────────────────────────────────
```

The predicate of the schema is telling us that the refund obtained is the current value of *input*. The display returns to zero, the "sold out" light, if it had been lit is switched to *off*, the temporary store is emptied and the value of *store* is unchanged.

6.6 ROBUST MACHINE OPERATIONS

The operations specified, apart from the *MoneyBack* operation, involve preconditions for their successful use. In order to produce robust operation schemas, we must now analyse these preconditions and produce appropriate error-handling schemas. In many cases the error handling schemas will involve more than just the reporting of suitable error messages.

Error messages

The precondition for the *CoinIn* schema to work successfully is the predicate $coin? \in \text{dom}\ value$. If this is violated then the input *coin?* is not recognised by the machine. A suitable error report might therefore be *invalid_coin*.

If we now investigate the *SuccessfulDrink* schema we see there are five preconditions. Careful analysis of these will reveal that it is still possible to obtain a drink even though some of these are not satisfied. We can obtain a drink with no change, when $light\ 1 = on$ and therefore $changeleft = 0$, but the other three preconditions are satisfied. We can also obtain a drink with partial change if all the preconditions are satisfied, but the predicate $changeleft \geq display - price\ b?$ no longer applies. Suitable error reports in each of these cases might therefore be *no_change_available* and *partial_change_given* respectively.

No drink will be obtained if the predicate $b? \in \text{dom}\ drink$ is violated. When this is the case an invalid selection has been made, and a suitable error report could well be *invalid_selection*. We also fail to obtain a drink if *display* $\geq$ *price b?* is violated. More money needs to be input, and a suitable error report might be *more_money_needed*. Finally, no drink is obtained if the condition *drinksleft*(*drink b?*) > 0 is violated. In other words the machine has sold out of the drink that is being requested. A suitable error report is therefore *sold_out*.

To build suitable error reporting schemas a free type called *REPORT* is defined as follows.

REPORT ::= *invalid_coin* | *invalid_selection* |
more_money_needed | *sold_out* | *no_change_available* |
partial_change_given | *operation_successful*

A *Success* schema to report accordingly when the predicates of an operation schema are successfully satisfied is also specified. The *Success* schema is as follows.

```
┌─Success──────────────────────
│ result! : REPORT
├──────────────────
│ result! = operation_successful
└──────────────────────────────
```

The robust *CoinIn* operation

A robust *CoinIn* operation may be defined as follows:

$RCoinIn \mathrel{\widehat=} (CoinIn \wedge Success) \vee CoinInError$

where the *CoinInError* schema is the following.

```
┌─CoinInError──────────────────
│ ΞMachine
│ coin? : COIN
│ result! : REPORT
├──────────────────
│ coin? ∉ dom value
│ result! = invalid_coin
└──────────────────────────────
```

The robust *SuccessfulDrink* operation

A robust *SuccessfulDrink* operation can be defined as follows.

$$RSuccessfulDrink \mathrel{\widehat=} (SuccessfulDrink \wedge Success) \vee SuccessfulDrinkError$$

The *SuccessfulDrinkError* schema is built up out of several schemas in the following way.

$SuccessfulDrinkError \mathrel{\widehat=} InvalidSelection \lor InsufficientMoney$
$\lor\ SoldOut \lor DrinkAndNoChange \lor DrinkAndSomeChange$

The *InvalidSelection* schema can be specified as follows.

```
┌─InvalidSelection──────────────
│ ΔMachine
│ ΞDisplay
│ ΞInformation
│ ΞInternalState
│ ΞMoneystore
│ b? : ℕ
│ report! : REPORT
├───────────────────────
│ b? ∉ dom drink
│ report! = invalid_selection
│ light' = light ⊕ {3 ↦ off}
└──────────────────────────────
```

The assumption is that while the machine is waiting for a correct sequence of buttons to be fed in, it switches the "sold out" light off, should it have been on, in order not to confuse or put off the user.

The *InsufficientMoney* schema operates in very much the same way as the *InvalidSelection* schema in that it specifies that the "sold out" light is also to be switched off, should it have been on.

```
┌─InsufficientMoney─────────────
│ ΔMachine
│ ΞDisplay
│ ΞInformation
│ ΞInternalState
│ ΞMoneyStore
│ b? : ℕ
│ report! : REPORT
├───────────────────────
│ b? ∈ dom drink
│ display < price b?
│
│ report! = more_money_needed
│ light' = light ⊕ {3 ↦ off}
└──────────────────────────────
```

The last of the error schemas for signalling why a drink is not dispensed is the *SoldOut* schema. This can be specified as follows.

```
─SoldOut──────────────────────
│ ΔMachine
│ ΞDisplay
│ ΞInformation
│ ΞInternalState
│ ΞMoneyState
│ b? : ℕ
│ report! : REPORT
├─────────────────────
│ b? ∈ dom drink
│ display ≥ price b?
│ amount(drink b?) = 0
│
│ report! = sold_out
│ light' = light ⊕ { 3 ↦ on}
└──────────────────────────
```

The *SoldOut* schema has the effect of switching the "sold out" light on.

The remaining two schemas describe the conditions necessary for a drink to be dispensed with no change, and with some change. The *DrinkAndNoChange* operation may be specified as follows.

```
─DrinkAndNoChange──────────────────────
│ ΔMachine
│ ΞInformation
│ b? : ℕ
│ dr! : DRINK
│ ch! : COIN ⇸ ℕ
│ result! : REPORT
├──────────────────────────
│ light 1 = on
│ b? ∈ dom drink
│ display ≥ price b?
│ drinksleft(drink b?) > 0
│
│ dr! = drink b?
│ ch! = change 0
│ result! = no_change_available
│ display' = 0
│ light' = light ⊕ {3 ↦ off}
│ changeleft' = 0
│ drinksleft' = drinksleft ⊕ {drink(b?) ↦
│                 drinksleft(drink b?) - 1}
│ input' = {c : dom input • c ↦ 0}
│ store' = {c : dom input • c ↦ (store c + input c)}
└──────────────────────────────────
```

The *DrinkAndNoChange* schema is very similar to the *SuccessfulDrink* schema. The main difference is that no change is given and the value of *changeleft* remains at the value zero.

The *DrinkAndSomeChange* schema is as follows.

```
──DrinkAndSomeChange──────────────────────
│ ΔMachine
│ ΞInformation
│ b? : ℕ
│ dr! : DRINK
│ ch! : COIN ⇸ ℕ
│ result! : REPORT
├──────────────────────────────
│ light 1 = off
│ b? ∈ dom drink
│ display ≥ price b?
│ drinksleft(drink b?) > 0
│ changeleft < display - price b?
│
│ dr! = drink b?
│ ch! = change(changeleft)
│ result! = partial_change_given
│
│ display' = 0
│ light' = light ⊕ {3 ↦ off, 1 ↦ on}
│ changeleft' = 0
│ drinksleft' = drinksleft ⊕ {drink(b?) ↦
│                  drinksleft(drink b?) - 1}
│ input' = {c : dom input • c ↦ 0}
│ store' = {c : dom input • c ↦ (store c + input c)}
└──────────────────────────────────────
```

Note that as the machine runs out of change, having been unable to pay out the total amount required, the "no change" light is set to the value *on*.

This concludes the specification of our drinks machine.

6.7 DISCUSSION

Compared with the specification of a large piece of software, such as an operating system, the specification here is modest. However, compared with the examples we have looked at before, it is substantially more complicated and does, in fact, have many features that are normally associated with more complex systems. It is therefore instructive to review and discuss the various stages we went through to arrive at the final version of the specification given above.

The first important point to note is that we started by considering the requirements for our software. Sorting out the exact nature of what is required at the beginning is of vital importance, because modifications at a later stage can often only be made at great cost and effort. Figure 6.1, together with discussion of the workings of the machine, are all part of the requirements analysis phase.

The next thing to note is that we partitioned the problem into manageable pieces, both when specifying the state of the machine and the operations that changed its state. The bottom-up approach afforded by the schema calculus was ideal for this partitioning, and it is important to note that writing simple schemas and then putting these together to build a system is an extremely natural, appealing and systematic way of attacking a problem.

As to the use of mathematics as a specification language, it is worth noting the expressive powers afforded by the simple mathematical structures that we have available so far. With just simple ideas of sets, logic and functions, we have been able to give a specification of a fairly complex system. In general, sets and functions will enable us to specify most systems, but there are richer mathematical structures available such as sequences and relations, which are discussed in the next two chapters.

Finally, although we have given a specification of the more important operations that one might wish to perform on the drinks machine, there are still several aspects about its operation which have not been specified. We have not specified how the machine is replenished with drinks and change, and how its strong box is emptied. Neither have we specified how information about drinks and their costs might be updated. These are all relatively simple operations and are left to the reader to specify as exercises. What should become evident when developing these additional specifications is the pay-off that comes from adopting a formal approach. Making modifications and enhancements are always that much easier when a formal specification of the original system is to hand.

CHAPTER 7

Sequences

7.1 INTRODUCTION

In the drinks machine specification that we have just considered, an alternative set of basic types that we might have parachuted in and worked with could have been

[*DRINK*, *COIN*, *BUTTON*]

Thus, instead of regarding drink codes as elements from the set of natural numbers $\mathbb{N}$, we could have built up these codes directly as a sequence of button values.

Sequences, which are the subject of this chapter, are useful constructs to have available for use in specifications, especially when structured objects, that we would normally call sequences, occur naturally in the system under consideration. Thus in our drinks machine specification, as well as having sequences of button values to model the drink codes, we could also have had sequences of coins to model the change that the machine might give.

We begin our study of sequences by giving a formal definition of what we mean by a sequence in terms of the mathematical objects that we have met so far.

7.2 FORMAL DEFINITION OF A SEQUENCE

A sequence can most conveniently be thought of as a finite function from an initial segment of the positive numbers to the set of elements that appear in the sequence. Thus the function definition

$$
\begin{aligned}
week == \{&1 \mapsto monday,\ 2 \mapsto tuesday,\ 3 \mapsto wednesday,\\
&4 \mapsto thursday,\ 5 \mapsto friday,\ 6 \mapsto saturday,\\
&7 \mapsto sunday\}
\end{aligned}
$$

describes the sequence of days that make up a week. The initial segment of the positive numbers that is involved here is the set

$$\{n : \mathbb{N} \mid 1 \leq n \leq 7\}$$

which, for short, is written as 1..7. The assumption always is that the function representing the sequence maps from the position in the sequence to the element of the sequence.

In general, given a set X, any sequence of elements from X will belong to a set known as the set of sequences of X, which we write as follows.

$$\text{seq } X$$

Thus, if the days of the week belong to some particular set called DAY, then *week*, as defined above, will belong to the set of sequences called seq DAY.

It is important to remember that sequences in Z are finite functions. If a partial function f, from X to Y, is known to be finite then there is a special way of signifying this when declaring the function (see example 1, Section 4.6 of Chapter 4). Instead of simply writing $f : X \nrightarrow Y$, we signify that f is finite by writing

$$f : X \twoheadrightarrow Y$$

This notation is used in the definition of seq X, which can be given as follows.

$$\text{seq } X == \{f : \mathbb{N} \twoheadrightarrow X \mid \text{dom } f = 1..\#f\}$$

Thus the set of sequences of X is the set of finite partial functions f, from $\mathbb{N}$ to X, where the domain of f is the initial segment $1..\#f$ of the positive numbers.

The following partial function, where the range elements stand for the characters themselves, is an example of a sequence from the set seq $CHAR$.

$$\{1 \mapsto s, 2 \mapsto e, 3 \mapsto q, 4 \mapsto u, 5 \mapsto e, 6 \mapsto n, 7 \mapsto c, 8 \mapsto e\}$$

It is just a formal way of describing what we mean by the word "sequence".

7.3 WRITING SEQUENCES

Writing out sequences as sets of maplets can become tedious. Hence a more concise notation, using angled brackets, has been devised.

Thus to represent the word "sequence" in a compact way using angled brackets we write

<*s*, *e*, *q*, *u*, *e*, *n*, *c*, *e*,>

All the information that is contained in the set of maplets is contained in this representation.

When a sequence contains no elements we say that the sequence is empty and represent it as follows.

< >

This is standard notation for an empty sequence, and is used in preference to the empty set { }.

7.4 FURTHER DEFINITIONS AND SEQUENCE OPERATIONS

To manipulate sequences in a specification we often need to refer to and use various operations defined on sequences. The following are some of the more commonly used functions and operations.

The length of a sequence

The length of a sequence is simply the cardinality of the set of maplets that represents the sequence. The length of a sequence will always be a finite number because sequences in Z are finite functions. The length of a sequence s is given by $\#s$, which is sometimes written as $|s|$. The length of <*s*,*e*,*q*,*u*,*e*,*n*,*c*,*e*> is thus 8, for example.

The *n*th element of a sequence

The nth element of a sequence s, where $1 \leq n \leq \#s$, is just the quantity $s(n)$, which is the value of the finite partial function s applied to the input value n. Clearly we cannot speak about the nth element of the empty sequence or the nth element of a sequence containing fewer than n elements. Thus the 4th element of the sequence we called *week* is *week*(4), which is *thursday*. The 2nd element of <*s*,*e*,*q*,*u*,*e*,*n*,*c*,*e*> is e, and so on. The first element of a sequence s is therefore $s(1)$ and its last element is $s(\#s)$. In general, brackets may be used if this aids clarity.

Concatenation

Concatenation is the operation which allows us to join two sequences to form a new one. To concatenate two sequences s and t, both from seq X, we attach t to the end of s. The result of the concatenation is a sequence which contains the elements of s followed by the elements of t. The concatenation of s and t is written

$$s \frown t$$

The resulting sequence can be defined formally in terms of s and t as follows.

$$s \frown t = s \cup \{n : \text{dom } t \bullet (n + \#s) \mapsto t(n)\}$$

It is clear from the definition that the elements in t are appended to those in s because their positions form the required segment given by $1 + \#s..\#t + \#s$.

Obvious properties of the concatenation operation are the following.

$$(s \frown t) \frown u = s \frown (t \frown u)$$

$$\langle\ \rangle \frown s = s$$

$$s \frown \langle\ \rangle = s$$

$$\#(s \frown t) = \#s + \#t$$

Squashing a sequence

Often we find that we need to be able to take a finite partial function of the kind $\mathbb{N} \nrightarrow X$ and turn it into a sequence. For example, let s be the function representing this sentence as a sequence of words. The sequence is therefore the following set of maplets.

$$\{1 \mapsto \mathit{for}, 2 \mapsto \mathit{example}, 3 \mapsto \mathit{let}, 4 \mapsto s, 5 \mapsto \mathit{be}, 6 \mapsto \mathit{the}, 7 \mapsto \mathit{function}, 8 \mapsto \mathit{representing}, 9 \mapsto \mathit{this}, 10 \mapsto \mathit{sentence}, 11 \mapsto \mathit{as}, 12 \mapsto a, 13 \mapsto \mathit{sequence}, 14 \mapsto \mathit{of}, 15 \mapsto \mathit{words}\}$$

If we range restrict s to words of length more than 7 letters then the restricted function is

$$\{7 \mapsto \mathit{function}, 8 \mapsto \mathit{representing}, 10 \mapsto \mathit{sentence}, 13 \mapsto \mathit{sequence}\}$$

Thus, if we wanted a sequence to contain the words in the specified sentence that possessed more than 7 letters, we would therefore have to turn this set of maplets into a sequence. The *squash* function is designed to do this. So if we wrote down

$$\mathit{squash}(\{7 \mapsto \mathit{function}, 8 \mapsto \mathit{representing}, 10 \mapsto \mathit{sentence}, 13 \mapsto \mathit{sequence}\})$$

the result would be the following sequence.

$$\langle \mathit{function}, \mathit{representing}, \mathit{sentence}, \mathit{sequence} \rangle$$

The *squash* function can be defined formally as a total function, for any set X, as follows.

$$squash : (\mathbb{N} \twoheadrightarrow\!\!\!\!\!\!\shortmid\;\; X) \longrightarrow \text{seq } X$$

$$\forall f : \mathbb{N} \twoheadrightarrow\!\!\!\!\!\!\shortmid\;\; X \bullet$$

$$f = \{\ \} \Rightarrow squash\ f = \langle\ \rangle$$
$$f \neq \{\ \} \Rightarrow \exists\ i : \mathbb{N} \mid i = min(\text{dom } f) \bullet$$
$$squash\ f = \langle f(i) \rangle \frown squash(\{i\} \mathbin{⩤} f)$$

The definition is recursive, which is typical of many operations defined on sequences. A sequence is an inherently recursive structure and this fact tends to manifest itself in many sequence-related definitions. What the definition is telling us, in the non-empty case, is that the first element in the squashed sequence is the range element of the maplet in f whose domain element is smallest. Concatenated to this will be the squashed sequence of what remains when this maplet has been removed.

Head of a sequence

When manipulating sequences it is convenient to be able to identify and refer to the first element of a sequence. This element is usually called the head of the sequence and is written as *head s*. The *head* function is only defined on non-empty sequences. The set of non-empty sequences, containing elements from the set X, is written as $\text{seq}_1 X$, and is the same as seq $X \setminus \{\langle\ \rangle\}$. The *head* function may be defined as follows for any set X.

$$head : \text{seq}_1 X \longrightarrow X$$

$$\forall\ s : \text{seq}_1 X \bullet$$
$$head\ s = s(1)$$

The last element of a sequence

As well as the head of a sequence, there is also the last element of a sequence written as *last s*. A generic definition for the function *last*, which applies for any set X, is the following.

$$last : \text{seq}_1 X \longrightarrow X$$

$$\forall\ s : \text{seq}_1 X \bullet$$
$$last\ s = s(\#s)$$

The tail of a sequence

When the head of a sequence is removed, what remains is known as the tail of the sequence. The *tail* function only applies to non-empty sequences, although it could well be that the tail of a sequence is the empty sequence. The *tail* function can conveniently be defined in terms of the *squash* function, for any set X, as follows.

$$tail : \mathrm{seq}_1 X \longrightarrow \mathrm{seq}\ X$$

$$\forall\, s : \mathrm{seq}_1 X \bullet tail\ s = squash(\{1\} \lhd s)$$

The front of a sequence

The front of a sequence is what remains when the last element is removed. As a function, *front* can only apply to non-empty sequences. Its generic definition, for any set X, is the following.

$$front : \mathrm{seq}_1 X \longrightarrow \mathrm{seq}\ X$$

$$\forall\, s : \mathrm{seq}_1 X \bullet front\ s = \{\#s\} \lhd s$$

Reversing a sequence

The reverse of a sequence s, often written *rev* s, is a sequence containing the same elements of s, but in reverse order. The reverse of an empty sequence is the empty sequence. The generic definition of *rev*, that holds for any set X, is as follows.

$$rev : \mathrm{seq}\ X \longrightarrow \mathrm{seq}\ X$$

$$\forall\, s : \mathrm{seq}\ X \bullet rev\ s = \{n : \mathrm{dom}\ s \bullet n \mapsto s(\#s - n + 1)\}$$

Restricting sequences

Given a sequence s, we may need to filter out elements that belong to a given set. The sequence written as

$$s \upharpoonright B$$

is the sequence which contains those elements of s, which are members of B, in the same order as in s. The generic definition of this filter function, which holds for any set X, is as follows.

$$
\begin{array}{|l}
\_\restriction\_ : \text{seq } X \times \mathbb{P}\, X \longrightarrow \text{seq } X \\
\hline
\forall\, s : \text{seq } X ;\ B : \mathbb{P}\, X \bullet \\
\quad s \restriction B = squash(s \rhd B)
\end{array}
$$

In the signature $\_\restriction\_$ means that when the filter function is applied to its arguments s and B, the result is written as $s \restriction B$. The notation being used is known as infix notation, which we meet again in Chapter 8 in connection with binary relations.

7.5 SEQUENCES IN ACTION : MODELLING A PETROL FILLING STATION

To see sequences in action we look at a situation where the use of sequences is extremely convenient. We consider the problem of describing the state of the queues that might form at the various petrol pumps in a typical filling station as cars arrive, are serviced, and leave. The aim is to exploit the power of Z to provide a simple model of queue behaviour, and to demonstrate that Z can be used in a wider context than just software specification. Z, as we shall see, is an excellent problem-definition language.

System assumptions

We assume that the filling station has several pumps and that cars arrive at a pump to be serviced. Each pump has an associated queue of cars waiting to be serviced. This queue may be empty. Cars can join any queue when they arrive and the assumption is that cars join the end of a queue. Cars may leave before being serviced and may well switch queues if the driver feels there is some advantage to be gained. Cars may leave a queue from any position within it, but can only be serviced if they are at the head of the queue.

The system state

We begin by parachuting into the specification the basic types that are needed. These are as follows.

$[PUMP, CAR]$

The basic type CAR corresponds to the set of all cars and not just to different makes of car. Two cars of the same make are therefore assumed to be different elements from the type set CAR. The state schema representing the queues of cars at our filling station may be written as follows.

```
┌─FillingStation─────────────────────────────
│ queues : PUMP ⇸ seq CAR
│ serviced : ℙ CAR
├──────────────────────────
│ ∀ p : dom queues •
│ #queues p = #ran(queues p)
│ serviced ∩ ran(queues p) = ∅
│
│ ∀ p₁ , p₂ : dom queues | p₁ ≠ p₂ •
│ ran(queues p₁) ∩ ran(queues p₂) = ∅
└─────────────────────────────────────────
```

The state is described in terms of a finite partial function *queues* from *PUMP* to seq *CAR* and a set called *serviced*. The finite partial function *queues* will give the sequence of cars queuing at any pump in the filling station. The set *serviced* is used to model the set of cars which have filled up with petrol, but have not yet left the filling station.

The schema predicate tells us that, for any pump at the filling station, the length of the queue at that pump is equal to the number of different cars in the queue. This condition ensures that a car cannot appear at several different places in a queue at one and the same time. The next condition, relating a queue to the set *serviced*, states that no car can be both in a queue and in the set of cars that have been serviced. The last predicate, which applies to any two queues, states that no car may appear in more than one queue at the same time. Obviously, if the filling station has only one pump at which queues may form, then this last predicate has no relevance and would be true vacuously.

Having described the general state of our filling station, it is instructive to specify an initial state. The following *InitFillingStation* schema sets up a filling station where all the queues at the pumps are empty and no cars have been serviced.

```
┌─InitFillingStation──────────────
│ FillingStation
├────────────────────────
│ ∀ p : dom queues • queues p = < >
│ serviced = ∅
└───────────────────────────────
```

Operations that change the state

Following this description of the state we now consider several operations that change the state. Let us begin by considering how the state of the queues is altered when a car arrives at the filling station and joins the end of a queue. The following *Arrives* schema specifies this situation.

```
┌─Arrives──────────────────────────────────────
│ ΔFillingStation
│ car? : CAR
│ p? : PUMP
├──────────────────────────────────
│ p? ∈ dom queues
│ ∀ p : dom queues • car? ∉ ran(queues p?)
│
│ queues' = queues ⊕ {p? ↦ queues(p?) ⁀ <car?>}
│ serviced' = serviced
└──────────────────────────────────────────────
```

We see that the pump *p?*, at which the car arrives, must be a pump at the filling station. Also, the car that arrives cannot already be in one of the queues at the filling station. The postcondition of the schema tells us that the function *queues* is updated by adding *car?* to the end of the queue at *p?* by concatenation, whilst the set of cars that have been serviced remains unchanged.

Having been in a queue for some time, a car may switch queues to join the end of another queue in order to gain some perceived advantage. The following *Switches* schema describes such a switching operation. Note that the car need not necessarily be the end car in a queue when the decision to swap occurs.

```
┌─Switches─────────────────────────────────────
│ ΔFillingStation
│ car? : CAR
│ p?, q? : PUMP
├──────────────────────────────────
│ p? ∈ dom queues
│ q? ∈ dom queues
│ q? ≠ p?
│ car? ∈ ran(queues p?)
│
│ queues' = queues ⊕ {p? ↦ squash(queues p? ⩥ {car}),
│                     q? ↦ queues(q?) ⁀ <car?>}
│ serviced' = serviced
└──────────────────────────────────────────────
```

For the switching operation to be successful we require that *p?* and *q?* are different pumps at the filling station and that the car involved in the switching is queuing at pump *p?*. The state variables are updated by taking *car?* out of the queue at *p?* and compacting this queue, and then adding *car?* to the queue at *q?*. The set *serviced*, once again, is left unchanged.

Having been in a queue for some time a driver may abandon all hope of being serviced and decide to leave the filling station! The following schema, called *LeavesUnhappy*, describes such a state of affairs.

```
┌─LeavesUnhappy──────────────────────────────
│ ΔFillingStation
│ car? : CAR
│ p? : PUMP
├──────────────────────────────
│ p? ∈ dom queues
│ car? ∈ ran(queues p?)
│ queues' = queues ⊕
│           {p? ↦ squash(queues p? ⩥ {car?})}
│ serviced' = serviced
└──────────────────────────────────────────
```

This operation is technically very similar to the *Switches* operation except that the car does not join a new queue.

A driver that patiently waits until his car is at the front of a queue will eventually be able to buy petrol and be serviced. The *Serviced* schema is as follows.

```
┌─Serviced──────────────────────────────────
│ ΔFillingStation
│ car? : CAR
│ p? : PUMP
├──────────────────────────────
│ p? ∈ dom queues
│ queues p? ≠ < >
│ car? = head(queues p?)
│ queues' = queues ⊕ {p? ↦ tail(queues p?)}
│ serviced' = serviced ∪ {car?}
└──────────────────────────────────────────
```

When the car leaves, the queue at *p?* becomes the same as its tail and the car is added to the set *serviced.*

The very last operation we need to specify is the one that enables a serviced car to drive away from the filling station to become a car that once again can be serviced by the same filling station. The *LeavesHappy* schema is as follows.

```
┌─LeavesHappy───────────────────────────────
│ ΔFillingStation
│ car? : CAR
├──────────────────────────────
│ car? ∉ {p : dom queues ; c : CAR |
│                c ∈ ran(queues p) • c}
│ car? ∈ serviced
│ queues' = queues
│ serviced' = serviced \ {car?}
└──────────────────────────────────────────
```

The two preconditions are needed (as opposed to the single condition *car?* $\in$ *serviced*) to prevent the data invariant being violated by a car that decides to join a queue having just been serviced. The rules of the filling station will require such a car to leave happy before arriving again.

7.6 EXERCISES

1. Specify an *insert* function that inserts an element $x : X$ into a sequence $s : \text{seq } X$ to become the nth element in the resulting sequence.

2. Specify a *cut* function that will cut a sequence $s : \text{seq } X$ into two sequences, preserving the order of the elements, where the nth element of s is the first element in the second of the two sequences that are created.

3. Specify a *sum* function recursively, that adds together elements belonging to a sequence of natural numbers and supplies their sum as output.

4. [illegible]llowing schema represents the state of an electronic score [illegible]r playing the game of darts.

ScoreSheet

$$\begin{array}{l} scores : PLAYER \twoheadrightarrow \text{seq } \mathbb{N} \\ requires : PLAYER \twoheadrightarrow \mathbb{N} \\ \hline \#scores \geqslant 1 \\ \text{dom } scores = \text{dom } requires \\ \forall\, p : \text{dom } scores \bullet \\ \quad requires\ p = 501 - sum(scores\ p) \\ \quad \text{ran}(scores\ p) \subseteq 0\,..\,180 \end{array}$$

(i) Write an appropriate initialisation schema.
(ii) Write an appropriate *AddScore* schema.
(iii) Write a schema called *WinningScore* that decides that the score to be added actually wins the game.

CHAPTER 8

Relations

8.1 INTRODUCTION

Many of the mathematical objects that we have met so far are examples of relations. A function, for example, can be thought of as a relation, in that an element in its domain is related to a corresponding element in its range. A set is another example of a relation, in the sense that all the elements in the set are related by virtue of being in the set. In fact any mathematical construct that involves elements that are somehow related can be regarded as a relation.

Of all the many different kinds of relations that there are, the most common one is probably the binary relation, and it is with this that we begin our study.

8.2 DEFINITION OF A BINARY RELATION

A binary relation is just a set of ordered pairs. For example, the set of ordered pairs given by

{(*allan*,*astra*), (*allan*,*pushbike*), (*sam*,*maestro*), (*sam*,*bmw*),
(*jane*,*pushbike*), (*jane*,*bmw*), (*anthony*,*volvo*), (*dave*,*fiesta*)}

can be thought of as making up a particular binary relation that we might call *drives*, in the sense that Allan drives an Astra, Allan drives a pushbike, and so on.

Similarly, the set of ordered pairs

{(0,< >), (1,<1p>), (2,<1p,1p>), (2,<2p>),
(3,<1p,1p,1p>), (3,<2p,1p>), (3,<1p,2p>), ...}

can be thought of as making up the binary relation called *change_for*.

Binary relations are thus subsets of Cartesian products. The binary relation *drives* can be viewed as a subset of the Cartesian product set *NAME* $\times$ *VEHICLE*, and *change_for* a subset of $\mathbb{N} \times$ seq *COIN*.

In general, a binary relation, whose typical element (x,y) is from the set $X \times Y$ is an object belonging to the set

$$\mathbb{P}(X \times Y)$$

Since other objects, particularly functions from X to Y, are also objects from this set, we signify a binary relation by writing the set of all possible binary relations between X and Y as

$$X \leftrightarrow Y$$

Clearly the set $X \leftrightarrow Y$ is identical to the power set $\mathbb{P}(X \times Y)$, and so

$$X \leftrightarrow Y == \mathbb{P}(X \times Y)$$

The binary relation corresponding to $X \times Y$ is the universal relation between X and Y, and the relation corresponding to the empty set is the null relation.

A binary relation, R, between sets X and Y can be declared in any signature by writing

$$R : X \leftrightarrow Y$$

To assert that an element x from X is related to an element y from Y, via the relation R, we write

$$(x,y) \in R$$

If we wish to make the same assertion using the infix notation, we write

$$x \; R \; y$$

and if we are using the prefix notation the equivalent assertion is made by writing

$$R(x,y)$$

In order to stress that a relation is a set we shall favour using the notation $(x,y) \in R$ to signify that x and y are related under R. A commonly used alternative to the ordered pair (x,y), when talking about a binary relation, is the maplet $x \mapsto y$. Thus an equivalent way of signifying that x and y are related via R is to write

$$(x \mapsto y) \in R$$

We shall use the ordered pair and maplet notation interchangeably.

8.3 SPECIFYING A BINARY RELATION

A binary relation can be specified in several ways.

Enumerating the elements in the relation
When there is no underlying rule to decide whether or not a pair belongs to a binary relation, then writing out all the ordered pairs that are known to belong to the relation is often the only way to specify the relation. In the first illustrative example above the binary relation had to be specified in this way. There is really no way of telling which vehicle someone drives. Clearly, specifying a binary relation in this way is only possible if the relation is finite. The elements of the relation can be written out as pairs or as maplets. The *drives* relation could just as easily have been written as the set

$$\{allan \mapsto astra,\ allan \mapsto pushbike,\ sam \mapsto maestro,\ sam \mapsto bmw,\ jane \mapsto pushbike,\ jane \mapsto bmw,\ anthony \mapsto volvo,\ dave \mapsto fiesta\}$$

Specifying the rule directly
A much more concise way of defining a binary relation is to specify the rule that relates the elements of each ordered pair in the relation. The binary relation *less_than*, for example, can be specified conveniently in this way.

$$less\_than : \mathbb{N} \leftrightarrow \mathbb{N}$$

$$\forall x,y : \mathbb{N} \bullet (x,y) \in less\_than \Leftrightarrow x < y$$

Specifying the rule is not always this easy. A definition may involve other mathematical objects. For example, a function called *sum*, from seq $\mathbb{N}$ to $\mathbb{N}$, that adds together the elements in the sequence, and a function called *value* from *COIN* to $\mathbb{N}$, could be used to give a definition of the *change_for* relation in terms of *sum* and *value* as follows.

$$change\_for : \mathbb{N} \leftrightarrow \text{seq } COIN$$

$$\forall x : \mathbb{N};\ y : \text{seq } COIN \bullet$$
$$(x,y) \in change\_for \Leftrightarrow x = sum(y \mathbin{;} value)$$

The specification of a particular binary relation can be recursive. The following generic recursive definition specifies the relation *member_of* where, in the pair (x,y), the element x is a member of the sequence y.

$$
\begin{array}{|l}
member\_of : X \leftrightarrow \mathrm{seq}\ X \\
\hline
\forall x : X ;\ y : \mathrm{seq}\ X \bullet \\
y = \langle\ \rangle \Rightarrow (x,y) \notin member\_of \\
y \neq \langle\ \rangle \Rightarrow (x,y) \in member\_of \Leftrightarrow x = head(y) \lor \\
\qquad\qquad (x,\ tail(y)) \in member\_of
\end{array}
$$

Defining a relation in terms of other relations

In exactly the same way that sets can be built from sets, and functions from functions, we can build up relations from relations. Thus, having defined one relation, it can be used again in the definition of other relations.

We consider several ways of doing this shortly but, to illustrate the concept, consider how we might define the binary relation *has_parent* in terms of the binary relations *has_father* and *has_mother*, in connection with ordinary kinship relations. Suppose we have defined these two binary relations and they are each of the form $PERSON \leftrightarrow PERSON$. The binary relation *has_parent* can then be specified as follows.

$$
\begin{array}{|l}
has\_parent : PERSON \leftrightarrow PERSON \\
\hline
has\_parent = has\_father \cup has\_mother
\end{array}
$$

All we have done is to use the simple set union operation to create the new relation. Before considering the other well-known ways of creating relations from relations, let us first define some additional terms that are needed in connection with binary relations.

8.4 FURTHER DEFINITIONS AND TERMS

Binary relations, like function, have domains and ranges.

The domain of a binary relation

Given a binary relation R between sets X and Y, the domain of R is the set of all members of X which are related to at least one member of Y by R. The domain of R is written in the normal way as

$$\mathrm{dom}\ R \quad \text{or} \quad \mathrm{dom}(R)$$

Using set comprehension notation we define the domain of R as

$$\mathrm{dom}\ R = \{x : X ;\ y : Y \mid (x \mapsto y) \in R \bullet x\}$$

The domain of our binary relation *drives*, for example, is therefore the set {*allan*, *sam*, *jane*, *anthony*, *dave*}.

The range of a binary relation
The range of a binary relation R between sets X and Y is the set of all members of Y to which at least one member of X is related by R. The range of R is written as

$$\text{ran } R \quad \text{or} \quad \text{ran}(R)$$

The definition of the range of R is

$$\text{ran } R = \{x : X \; ; \; y : Y \mid (x \mapsto y) \in R \bullet y\}$$

The set $\{astra, \; pushbike, \; maestro, \; bmw, \; volvo, \; fiesta\}$ is thus the range of our *drives* relation.

The relational image of a set
The domain of a binary relation maps over to the range set, and therefore a subset S of the domain will map over to a corresponding subset of the range. This corresponding subset is known as the relational image of S through the relation. Thus, given a set S from the power set of X, and a binary relation R between X and Y, the relational image of S through R, written as $R \llparenthesis S \rrparenthesis$, is defined as follows.

$$R \llparenthesis S \rrparenthesis = \{x : X \; ; \; y : Y \mid x \in S \land (x \mapsto y) \in R \bullet y\}$$

It is worth noting that $R \llparenthesis S \rrparenthesis$ could well be empty, and will be whenever S and dom R are disjoint sets. In connection with our *drives* example we see that $drives \llparenthesis \{allan, \; jane\} \rrparenthesis = \{astra, \; pushbike, \; bmw\}$.

8.5 OPERATIONS ON BINARY RELATIONS

We now have all the terminology that we need to look at various ways of creating new relations from ones that have already been defined. The operations we consider are precisely those that we met previously in Chapter 5 for creating new functions. Thus we shall look in turn at restricting and anti-restricting a relation, at relational composition, and at inverse relations. Since these operations are exactly analogous to those for functions, we list them without too much discussion. We do, however, give examples to illustrate their use.

Domain restriction
The relation R, between X and Y, that is domain restricted to the set A from the power set of X, is written as $A \lhd R$ and is the set given by

$$A \lhd R = \{x : X \; ; \; y : Y \mid x \in A \land (x \mapsto y) \in R \bullet x \mapsto y\}$$

Thus $\{sam, allan\} \lhd drives$ is the following relation.

$$\{sam \mapsto bmw,\ sam \mapsto maestro,\ allan \mapsto pushbike,\ allan \mapsto astra\}$$

Domain subtraction or anti-restriction

If we restrict the domain of the relation R, between X and Y, to the set $X \setminus B$, where B is from the power set of X, then the domain subtracted (or anti-restricted) relation R is written $B \ntriangleleft R$ and is the set given by

$$B \ntriangleleft R = \{x : Y ; y : Y \mid x \notin B \land (x \mapsto y) \in R \bullet x \mapsto y\}$$

For the *drives* relation it follows that $\{jane, sam, dave\} \ntriangleleft drives$ is the following relation.

$$\{allan \mapsto astra,\ allan \mapsto pushbike,\ anthony \mapsto volvo\}$$

Range restriction and subtraction

The relation R, between X and Y, that has been range restricted to the set C, from the power set of Y, is written $R \rhd C$. Similarly, the relation R that does not contain in its range any element in the set D, also from the power set of Y, is written $R \ntriangleright D$. These two restricted relations can be defined as follows.

$$R \rhd C = \{x : X ; y : Y \mid y \in C \land (x \mapsto y) \in R \bullet y\}$$

$$R \ntriangleright D = R \rhd (Y \setminus D)$$

Thus it follows, for example, that the relation $has\_parent \ntriangleright FATHER$, where the set $FATHER$ is the set of people who are fathers, is the relation *has_mother*.

Relational composition

The result of composing a binary relation R, between X and Y, with a binary relation S, between Y and Z, is a binary relation between X and Z that is written $S \circ R$ or $R \mathbin{;} S$. Relational composition is exactly analogous to function composition, and the definition of the process is similar. Thus, given R and S as above, $S \circ R$ or $R \mathbin{;} S$ is the following binary relation.

$$\{x : X ; y : Y ; z : Z \mid (x \mapsto y) \in R \land (y \mapsto z) \in S \bullet x \mapsto z\}$$

By way of an illustration of relational composition, let the binary relation *office* between $ROOM$ and $NAME$ be the following set of maplets.

$\{313 \mapsto allan,\ 310 \mapsto dave,\ 312 \mapsto anthony,$
$310 \mapsto mike,\ 316 \mapsto sam,\ 316 \mapsto maggie\}$

The binary relation $office \mathbin{;} drives$ is thus

$\{313 \mapsto astra,\ 313 \mapsto pushbike,\ 310 \mapsto fiesta,$
$312 \mapsto volvo,\ 316 \mapsto maestro,\ 316 \mapsto bmw\}$

The inverse of a binary relation
The inverse of a binary relation R from X to Y is written as $R^{\sim}$ or R^{-1}. If $x \mapsto y$ is a maplet in R then $y \mapsto x$ is a maplet in $R^{\sim}$, and vice versa. The binary relation $R^{\sim}$ can thus be defined as follows.

$$R^{\sim} = \{x : X \ ; \ y : Y \mid (x \mapsto y) \in R \bullet y \mapsto x\}$$

We might therefore define a binary relation *is_driven_by* to be $drives^{\sim}$, which is the following set of maplets.

$\{astra \mapsto allan,\ pushbike \mapsto allan,\ maestro \mapsto sam,$
$bmw \mapsto sam,\ pushbike \mapsto jane,\ bmw \mapsto jane,$
$volvo \mapsto anthony,\ fiesta \mapsto dave\}$

Obvious examples of inverses are the following.

$$greater\_than = less\_than^{\sim}$$

$$owned\_by = owns^{\sim}$$

$$has\_child = has\_parent^{\sim}$$

A property of any binary relation R, from X to Y, is that when composed with its inverse it yields a subset of the identity relation on X. The domain of the identity relation will be equal to the domain of the binary relation R. The identity relation is often called the identity function, because it behaves as a function.

8.6 RELATIONS IN GENERAL

Although we have spent some considerable time discussing binary relations, it is important to note that not all relations are binary relations. A general n-place relation on the sets $T_1, T_2, \ldots, T_n$ is just a set of n-tuples where elements of the relation belong to the Cartesian product $T_1 \times T_2 \times \ldots \times T_n$. Thus the set of secondhand cars for sale in a car showroom could be represented by a relation called *current_stock*, for example, whose elements belonged to the Cartesian product

$$MAKE \times MODEL \times YEAR$$

Or entries in an address book could be regarded as a relation called *addresses*, whose elements belonged to the set

$$NAME \times ADDRESS \times PHONE$$

and so on.

A general *n*-place relation, R, on the sets T_1, T_2, ..., T_n is thus a subset of the Cartesian product $T_1 \times T_2 \times \ldots \times T_n$ and in any signature involving R we would write

$$R : \mathbb{P}(T_1 \times T_2 \times \ldots \times T_n)$$

Clearly, a 2-place relation is a binary relation and a 1-place, or unary, relation is a set.

With a general *n*-place relation there is no concept of a domain or a range and it is meaningless, therefore, to talk about domain or range restricting such a relation. However, by imposing additional constraints on some or all of the sets T_1, T_2, ..., T_n it is possible to restrict a relation that has previously been defined on these sets. It is also important to note that, because *n*-place relations do not possess domains and ranges, it is difficult to think of composing such relations, one with another, or of forming inverses. Nevertheless, *n*-place relations are useful constructs for describing all kinds of structured objects, and an example illustrating their use is given in the next section.

8.7 WORKED EXAMPLES

Example 1 : simple operations on binary relations

This first example is designed to demonstrate how the operations on binary relations considered in Section 8.5 can be used in simple modelling contexts.

- If *skilled_in* is a binary relation between *PERSON* and *SUBJECT* and *useful_for* is a binary relation between *SUBJECT* and *CAREER*, obtain possible expressions for

  (i) the set of people skilled in the subject *formal_methods*
  (ii) the relation that would specify the careers for which it was deemed *formal_methods* were not useful
  (iii) the relation that specifies the careers for which people are suited
  (iv) the careers that *peter* could pursue
  (v) the set of careers to which both *sally* and *mark* would be suited

Solution

(i) The set of people skilled in the topic *formal_methods* makes up the domain of *skilled_in* after it has been range restricted to the set containing *formal_methods*. Thus the set can be written as

$$\mathrm{dom}(skilled\_in \rhd \{formal\_methods\})$$

Note that an alternative expression would be the following, which involves the inverse of *skilled_in* and the resulting image of the set containing *formal_methods*.

$$skilled\_in^{\sim} (\!| \{formal\_methods\} |\!)$$

(ii) The relation that specifies the careers for which it is deemed *formal_methods* were not useful is

$$\{formal\_methods\} \lhd useful\_for$$

(iii) The relation that links people to careers for which they are deemed to be suited can be obtained by composing *skilled_in* with *useful_for*, to give a binary relation between *PERSON* and *CAREER*. This relation can therefore be written as

$$skilled\_in \ ⨾ \ useful\_for$$

(iv) The careers that *peter* could pursue can be specified as the image of {*peter*} through the relation just defined. The set is therefore given by

$$skilled\_in \ ⨾ \ useful\_for \ (\!| \{peter\} |\!)$$

(v) The set of careers for which both *sally* and *mark* are suited is the intersection of the two sets of careers to which each are suited. This set is thus

$$(skilled\_in \ ⨾ \ useful\_for \ (\!| \{sally\} |\!)) \cap (skilled\_in \ ⨾ \ useful\_for \ (\!| \{mark\} |\!))$$

Example 2 : specifying a binary relation
The aim of this example is to demonstrate the power of recursion in specifying particular binary relations.

- Given the binary relation called *has_parent*, supply a recursive definition of the binary relation *has_ancestor* in connection with ordinary family relationships. Give a similar definition for the relation *has_descendant* in terms of the relation *has_child*.

Solution
The relation *has_ancestor* can be specified recursively as follows.

$$
\begin{array}{|l}
has\_ancestor : PERSON \leftrightarrow PERSON \\
\hline
\forall x,y : PERSON \bullet \\
\quad (x,y) \in has\_ancestor \Leftrightarrow (x,y) \in has\_parent \lor \\
\quad \exists z : PERSON \bullet (x,z) \in has\_parent \land \\
\quad\quad (z,y) \in has\_ancestor
\end{array}
$$

Thus, x has ancestor y is equivalent to x having y as parent, or having z as parent and z having y as ancestor.

The binary relation *has_descendant* can be recursively defined in terms of *has_child* in an analogous fashion as

$$
\begin{array}{|l}
has\_descendant : PERSON \leftrightarrow PERSON \\
\hline
\forall x,y : PERSON \bullet \\
\quad (x,y) \in has\_descendant \Leftrightarrow (x,y) \in has\_child \lor \\
\quad \exists z : PERSON \bullet (x,z) \in has\_child \land \\
\quad\quad (z,y) \in has\_descendant
\end{array}
$$

Note that $has\_descendant = has\_ancestor^{\sim}$.

Example 3 : specifying Newton's method as a general *n*–place relation
This example is taken from mathematics, and demonstrates the power of the Z notation for specifying numerical techniques for solving equations of the form $f(x) = 0$.

- Specify, with accompanying explanation, the conditions necessary for the Newton–Raphson method to supply a root of the differentiable function $f : \mathbb{R} \to \mathbb{R}$.

Solution
Readers who are not familiar with the Newton–Raphson technique can skip this example without serious detriment! However, those who have used the method should find the example interesting.

In the Newton–Raphson technique, if x_0 is an approximation to the root in question, then a better approximation is the value given by

$$x_1 = x_0 - f(x_0)/f'(x_0)$$

where $f'(x_0)$ is the derived function of f evaluated at x_0 and the symbol / is used to represent division. Clearly, by repeatedly replacing x_0 by x_1 and obtaining successively better approximations to the root, the value of the root can be determined to within any desired accuracy.

The following specification states the conditions necessary for a root to have been found, within N iterations of the method, using the criterion that successive approximations to the root differ by no more than some specified amount e, in order to terminate the iteration. The specification is written as a general n-place relation.

$$newton : \mathbb{P}((\mathbb{R} \to \mathbb{R}) \times \mathbb{R} \times \mathbb{R} \times \mathbb{R} \times \mathbb{N} \times \mathbb{N} \times \mathbb{N})$$

$$\begin{array}{l}
\forall\ f : \mathbb{R} \to \mathbb{R}\ ;\ x_0,\ x,\ e\ : \mathbb{R}\ ;\ n_0,\ n,\ N : \mathbb{N} \mid e > 0 \bullet \\
\quad ((f,\ x_0,\ x,\ e,\ n_0,\ n,\ N) \in newton \Leftrightarrow \\
\quad (x = x_0 - f(x_0)/f'(x_0) \wedge abs(x - x_0) \leqslant e \wedge \\
\quad n = n_0 + 1 \wedge n \leqslant N) \vee \\
\quad (\exists\ x_1 : \mathbb{R}\ ;\ n_1 : \mathbb{N} \bullet \\
\quad\ x_1 = x_0 - f(x_0)/f'(x_0) \wedge abs(x_1 - x_0) > e \wedge \\
\quad\ n_1 = n_0 + 1 \wedge n_1 < N \wedge \\
\quad\ (f,\ x_1,\ x,\ e,\ n_1,\ n,\ N) \in newton)
\end{array}$$

Clearly some explanation is needed, so let us start by explaining what the variables involved in the relation represent.

- f is the real-valued function whose root we aim to find
- x_0 is the current approximation to the root after n_0 applications of the iterative formula
- x is the root that differs by no more than e from the previous iterate
- n is the number of iterations required to obtain the root
- N is the maximum number of iterations permitted

The specification can now be interpreted as follows. If the 7-tuple $(f, x_0, x, e, n_0, n, N)$ belongs to the relation *newton*, then two possibilities exist. In the first case the next application of the iterative formula will furnish the root, so necessarily $x = x_0 - f(x_0)/f'(x_0)$, $abs(x-x_0) \leqslant e$, $n = n_0 + 1$, and $n < N$. Alternatively, the next application will not furnish the root, but give rise to x_1 and n_1 for which $x_1 = x_0 - f(x_0)/f'(x_0)$, $abs(x_1-x_0) > e$, $n_1 = n_0 + 1$, $n_1 < N$, and for which the new 7-tuple, given by $(f, x_1, x, e, n_1, n, N)$, belongs to *newton*.

Example 4 : specifying a simple library system

This last example involves the use of binary relations within schemas, and shows how they can be updated and inspected as various operations involving them are performed.

pecify a simple library system that (i) monitors which copies in its collection are on the shelves and which are out on loan, (ii) monitors the books and copies which users have out on loan, (iii) allows new users to join the library, (iv) allows a new copy of a book to be added to the library, and (v) enables existing users to borrow a copy of a book, provided it is available for borrowing.

Solution
First we parachute into the specification the basic types that we shall need.

$[COPY, BOOK, PERSON]$

COPY is the set of copies of books from the set *BOOK*. Users of the library are people from the set *PERSON*.

Next we specify the state of our library. To simplify the specification, it is useful to structure the state schema in such a way as to separate out information relating to books from information relating to borrowers. The information relating to books is contained in the following schema called *Stocks*

```
┌─Stocks──────────────────────────
│ copies_in, copies_out : ℙ COPY
│ copies : BOOK ↔ COPY
├──────────────────────
│ copies_in ∩ copies_out = ∅
│ copies_in ∪ copies_out = ran copies
└─────────────────────────────────
```

and information about borrowers is given in the following *Borrowers* schema.

```
┌─Borrowers───────────────────
│ users : ℙ PERSON
│ loans : PERSON ↔ COPY
├──────────────────────
│ dom loans ⊆ users
└─────────────────────────────
```

The identifiers *copies_in* and *copies_out* are the copies of books that are respectively on the shelves and out on loan. The binary relation called *copies* keeps a record of the copies of different books that exist in the library. The set of borrowers is called *users*, and the binary relation called *loans* monitors the copies of books a user has out on loan. These two schemas form the *Library* schema as follows.

```
┌─Library──────────────────────
│ Stocks
│ Borrowers
├──────────────────────
│ ran loans = copies_out
└─────────────────────────────
```

Library is the system state schema, and its predicate ensures that all copies of books out on loan are accounted for.

An initialisation schema for the library system can be written as follows.

```
┌─InitLibrary──────────────────
│ Library
├──────────────────────
│ copies_in = ∅
│ copies_out = ∅
│ copies = ∅
│ users = ∅
│ loans = ∅
└─────────────────────────────
```

This assumes that initially we have a library with no books and no users.

We now consider operations that will change the state of the library. The *Join* schema specifies how a new user joins the library.

```
┌─Join─────────────────────────
│ ΔLibrary
│ ΞStocks
│ new_user? : PERSON
├──────────────────────
│ new_user? ∉ users
│ users' = users ∪ {new_user?}
│ loans' = loans
└─────────────────────────────
```

The precondition is telling us that *new_user?* should not belong to *users*. In this case *new_user?* is added to the set *users*, without affecting *loans*. The signature of the schema informs us that none of the state variables in *Stocks* is changed by this operation.

A new copy of a book (either known or new to the library) is added to the library's collection in a way that is specified by the following *AddCopy* schema. Adding a new copy in no way affects any of the state variables in the *Borrowers* schema.

```
┌─AddCopy──────────────────────────
│ ΔLibrary
│ ΞBorrowers
│ new_copy? : COPY
│ book? : BOOK
├──────────────────────
│ (book? ↦ copy?) ∉ copies
│ copies_in' = copies_in ∪ {copy?}
│ copies_out' = copies_out
│ copies' = copies ∪ {book? ↦ copy?}
└──────────────────────────────────
```

The last operation we specify, that changes the state of the library, is the operation of issuing a copy of a book to a user. The operation is called *IssueCopy* and can be specified as follows.

```
┌─IssueCopy────────────────────────
│ ΔLibrary
│ user? : PERSON
│ copy? : COPY
├──────────────────────
│ user? ∈ users
│ copy? ∈ copies_in
│ copies_in' = copies_in \ {copy?}
│ copies_out' = copies_out ∪ {copy?}
│ copies' = copies
│ users' = users
│ loans' = loans ∪ {user? ↦ copy?}
└──────────────────────────────────
```

We now specify just one querying operation, namely that which queries *loans* and *copies* to find out which copies and which books a user of the library has out on loan. Such a querying operation may be specified as follows.

```
┌─QueryUserForBooks────────────────
│ ΞLibrary
│ user? : PERSON
│ borrowed_copies! : ℙ COPY
│ borrowed_books! : ℙ BOOK
├──────────────────────
│ user? ∈ users
│ borrowed_copies = loans ⦇ {user?} ⦈
│ borrowed_books = dom(copies ▷ loans ⦇ {user?} ⦈)
└──────────────────────────────────
```

Here the required sets of copies and books are specified conveniently using relational image and range restriction respectively.

This concludes our study of the simple library system.

8.8 EXERCISES

1. Produce a schema, called *Withdraw*, that specifies how an old copy of a book is withdrawn from the library system above.

2. Specify a querying operation called *QueryForAvailability* that checks whether a book is available for borrowing.

3. Produce robust user interfaces for all the operations considered in connection with the library system.

CHAPTER 9

Generating programs from specifications : refinement

9.1 INTRODUCTION

The mathematics we have considered has been primarily the mathematics needed to enable us to write formal specifications. However, once a specification has been created and we are satisfied that it accurately expresses our intentions, then the task of developing the coding must begin.

In this chapter we consider the issues involved in generating programs from specifications. Although we see that new mathematics is needed to support this activity, namely the mathematics of proof, we defer a study of this until the next chapter. In many ways, therefore, this chapter serves as a scene-setter for the next one.

Although Z is similar in many respects to languages such as PROLOG, its structure is quite different from the usual procedural languages such as Pascal, FORTRAN or BASIC. To implement a Z specification in a Pascal-like language we have first to refine the specification. Refinement is the process whereby an abstract specification is turned into a concrete design, and eventually into coding. In refining a specification it is vital that the ability to reason formally about what has been written is still retained. To ensure that this is the case concrete designs, as they are produced, are still expressed as schemas in Z, and theorems are proved to establish that the concrete designs implement the original specification. When a concrete design is sufficiently well developed to be written in code, the code is then produced and, once again, theorems are proved to establish rigorously that the coding matches the specification.

Of course, before any concrete designs or coding are produced, it is vital to check the original abstract specification against the user's requirements. This task is made easier if a rapid prototype of the system is available, that is faithful to the specification. Rapid prototyping is often carried out in languages such as PROLOG, and is one way of checking out the specification and validating with the customer that the correct system is being built.

As an example of the stages involved in refinement, but without giving proofs, we look at the systematic way in which a simple specification might be implemented in a language such as Pascal. The system we look at is the security system that we studied in some considerable detail in Chapter 3. The eventual coding will be Pascal-like pseudocode.

9.2 CHOOSING A CONCRETE DATA STRUCTURE

It is important to realise that constructs such as sets and functions, might not be readily available as data structures in the target language of an implementation. When choosing a concrete data structure it is important to work with structures that can be readily set up on a machine. Since abstract data structures such as sets and functions can be represented as arrays in a computer, then it is sensible to choose arrays as the concrete data structure for the state variables in our security system.

We shall assume, for convenience at this stage, that infinite arrays are available for our first refinement. Remembering that the state variables in our security system are the sets *in*, *out* and *users*, we choose to represent the state variables by the following arrays.

in1 : **array**[1..] **of** *STAFF_ID*

out1 : **array**[1..] **of** *STAFF_ID*

users1 : **array**[1..] **of** *STAFF_ID*

The names *in1*, *out1*, *users1* have been chosen simply to signify that this is the first refinement.

Such arrays can be modelled in Z by the following total functions

$in1 : \mathbb{N}_1 \longrightarrow STAFF\_ID$

$out1 : \mathbb{N}_1 \longrightarrow STAFF\_ID$

$users1 : \mathbb{N}_1 \longrightarrow STAFF\_ID$

where the set $\mathbb{N}_1$ is equal to the set $\mathbb{N} \setminus \{0\}$. The functions are total, and not partial, because when an array is set up each entry in the array is allocated some particular initial value, equal to *null_id* say, so that all the array elements are totally defined.

9.3 SPECIFYING THE NEW SYSTEM STATE

Having chosen the concrete data structure for the problem, the next stage is to give a description of the system state using this new data structure. We do this via a new state schema called *State1*. In order to capture all the information about the system in terms of arrays, and therefore total functions, it will be necessary to use extra system variables. These variables are x, y, z and they tell us how much of each respective array is occupied by an element from *STAFF_ID* that is not simply a null entry. The *State1* schema for our security system can thus be written as follows.

$$
\begin{array}{|l}
\textit{State1} \\
\hline
in1,\ out1,\ users1 : \mathbb{N}_1 \longrightarrow STAFF\_ID \\
x,\ y,\ z : \mathbb{N} \\
\hline
\forall\, i_1, i_2 : 1..x \bullet i_1 \neq i_2 \Rightarrow in1(i_1) \neq in1(i_2) \\
\forall\, j_1, j_2 : 1..y \bullet j_1 \neq j_2 \Rightarrow out1(j_1) \neq out1(j_2) \\
\forall\, k_1, k_2 : 1..z \bullet k_1 \neq k_2 \Rightarrow users1(k_1) \neq users1(k_2) \\
\\
\forall\, i : \mathbb{N}_1 \mid i > x \bullet in1(i) = null\_id \\
\forall\, j : \mathbb{N}_1 \mid j > y \bullet out1(j) = null\_id \\
\forall\, k : \mathbb{N}_1 \mid k > z \bullet users1(k) = null\_id \\
\\
\mathrm{ran}(1..x \lhd in1) \cap \mathrm{ran}(1..y \lhd out1) = \{\} \\
\mathrm{ran}(1..x \lhd in1) \cup \mathrm{ran}(1..y \lhd out1) \\
\qquad\qquad\qquad = \mathrm{ran}(1..z \lhd users1) \\
\hline
\end{array}
$$

The variables x, y and z are often called high–water marks. The first three lines of the predicate capture the fact that duplicates are not allowed in any given array. If duplicates did occur, then the original abstract specification involving sets would not have been implemented, as duplicates are not allowed in sets. The next three lines of the predicate are used to assign *null_id* entries to those parts of the arrays that are not occupied by substantive *staff_id* values. The last two lines capture the essence of the *State* data invariant set down originally in the abstract specification of the system state.

9.4 THE ABSTRACTION RELATION

In order to reason about the concrete specification being built, in comparison with the information set down in the original abstract specification, the two state schemas must be related to one another. We do this by writing down an abstraction relation, which here is called *Abs*. Through *Abs* we specify precisely how *in*, *out*, *users*, *in1*, *out1*, *users1* and x, y, z are related.

The *Abs* schema that relates these variables is as follows.

```
┌─Abs──────────────────────────────
│ State
│ State1
├──────────────────────────
│ in    = {i : 1..x • in1(i)}
│ out   = {j : 1..y • out1(j)}
│ users = {k : 1..z • users1(k)}
└──────────────────────────────────
```

9.5 THE NEW INITIAL STATE

The initial state expressed in terms of the new data structure can be specified via the following *InitState1* schema.

```
┌─InitState1───────────────────────
│ State1
├──────────────────────────
│ x = 0
│ y = 0
│ z = 0
│ ∀ i : ℕ₁ • in1(i) = null_id
│ ∀ j : ℕ₁ • out1(j) = null_id
│ ∀ k : ℕ₁ • users1(k) = null_id
└──────────────────────────────────
```

The high-water marks are set to zero and the arrays are filled with *null_id* entries. The *InitState1* schema is the concrete version of the original *InitState* schema that was set up with no *staff_id* codes in it.

9.6 REFINING THE REST OF THE SPECIFICATION

We now refine the rest of the specification by rewriting all the schemas of our original specification in terms of the new data structure and the new variable names.

The robust *Add1* operation

The schema definition of *RAdd1* can be given by analogy with the definition of the *RAdd* operation. Explicitly we have

$$RAdd1 \triangleq (Add1 \wedge Success) \vee AlreadyUser1$$

where the new *Add1* schema is as follows.

```
Add1
ΔState1
new? : STAFF_ID
─────────────
∀ k : 1..z • users1(k) ≠ new?
x' = x
in1' = in1
y' = y + 1
out1' = out1 ⊕ {y' ↦ new?}
z' = z + 1
users1' = users1 ⊕ {z' ↦ new?}
```

Note that the precondition for the abstract *Add* operation to work, which was *new?* ∉ *users*, has now been written in a more concrete way that involves searching the *users1* array. The high-water marks and state variables are updated in a way consistent with the original abstract specification for the *Add* operation.

The *Success* schema is exactly as before and the *AlreadyUser1* schema can be written as follows.

```
AlreadyUser1
ΞState1
new? : STAFF_ID
result! : REPORT
─────────────
∃ k : 1..z • users(k) = new?
result! = already_user
```

The robust *CheckIn1* operation

The robust *CheckIn1* operation can be specified by analogy with the specification of the abstract *CheckIn* operation as

$$RCheckIn1 \mathrel{\hat{=}} (CheckIn1 \wedge Success) \vee CheckIn1Error$$

and, by analogy with the way we defined *CheckInError*, we define *CheckIn1Error* as follows.

$$CheckIn1Error \mathrel{\hat{=}} StaffIn1 \vee NotUser1$$

The specification of the *CheckIn1* operation is given by the following schema.

```
┌─CheckIn1──────────────────────────────
│ ΔState1
│ staff? : STAFF_ID
├──────────────────────────
│ ∃ j : 1..y • out(j) = staff?
│ x' = x + 1
│ in1' = in1 ⊕ {x' ↦ staff?}
│ y' = y - 1
│ out1' = out1 ⊕ {out1⁻¹(staff?) ↦ out1(y),
│                 y ↦ null_id}
│ z' = z
│ users1' = users1
└──────────────────────────────────────
```

This specifies how to remove *staff?* from the *out1* array so that the resulting array is compact and its high-water mark is $y - 1$. This is done by identifying its position in the array using the inverse function $out1^{-1}$. Having identified its position in the array the corresponding array element is replaced by the last element in the array and the last element is replaced by a *null_id* entry. Specifying how an operation is to be carried out, in more concrete terms than was previously specified, is an example of operation refinement.

The *StaffIn1* and *NotUser1* schemas are as follows.

```
┌─StaffIn1──────────────────
│ ΞState1
│ staff? : STAFF_ID
│ result! : REPORT
├──────────────────
│ ∃ i : 1..x • in1(i) = staff?
│ result! = already_in
└──────────────────────────
```

```
┌─NotUser1──────────────────
│ ΞState1
│ staff? : STAFF_ID
│ result! : REPORT
├──────────────────
│ ∀ k : 1..z • users1(k) ≠ staff?
│ result! = not_known
└──────────────────────────
```

The robust *CheckOut1* operation

This operation is specified in a very similar fashion to the robust *CheckIn1* operation. At the schema level we have

$$RCheckOut1 \mathrel{\widehat=} (CheckOut1 \land Success) \lor CheckOut1Error$$

$$CheckOut1Error \mathrel{\widehat=} StaffOut1 \lor NotUser1$$

The schema *CheckOut1* can be written as follows

```
┌─CheckOut1──────────────────────────────────
│ ΔState1
│ staff? : STAFF_ID
├────────────────────────────────
│ ∃ i : 1..x • in(i) = staff?
│
│ x' = x - 1
│ in1' = in1 ⊕ {in1⁻¹(staff?) ↦ in1(x),
│               x ↦ null_id}
│ y' = y + 1
│ out1' = out1 ⊕ {x' ↦ staff?}
│
│ z' = z
│ users1' = users1
└────────────────────────────────────────────
```

and the *StaffOut1* schema is the following.

```
┌─StaffOut1──────────────────────────────────
│ ΞState1
│ staff? : STAFF_ID
│ result! : REPORT
├────────────────────────────────
│ ∃ j : 1..y • out1(j) = staff?
│ result! = already_out
└────────────────────────────────────────────
```

The *NotUser1* schema has already been defined.

The robust *Remove1* operation

This robust operation may be specified at the schema level as follows.

$$RRemove1 \mathrel{\widehat=} (Remove1 \land Success) \lor Remove1Error$$

$$Remove1Error \mathrel{\widehat=} StillIn1 \lor NotUser1$$

The *RRemove* schema can be written in the following way.

```
┌─RRemove──────────────────────────────────────
│ ΔState1
│ staff? : STAFF_ID
├──────────────────────────────────
│ ∃ j : 1..y • out1(j) = staff?
│ x' = x
│ in1' = in1
│
│ y' = y - 1
│ out1' = out1 ⊕ {out1⁻¹(staff?) ↦ out1(y),
│                    y ↦ null_id}
│ z' = z - 1
│ users1' = users1 ⊕ {users1⁻¹(staff?) ↦
│                    users1(z), z ↦ null_id}
└──────────────────────────────────────────────
```

The *StillIn1* schema is defined as follows.

```
┌─StillIn1──────────────────────────
│ ΞState1
│ staff? : STAFF_ID
│ result! : REPORT
├──────────────────────────
│ ∃ i : 1..x • in1(i) = staff?
│ result! = still_in
└──────────────────────────────────
```

Again, the *NotUser1* schema, in the definition of the robust *Remove1* operation, has been defined previously.

Robust query operations

Robust querying operations, that give the identity codes of staff who are in the building, out of the building, and valid users of the building, can be defined at the schema level as follows.

$$RQueryForIn1 \mathrel{\widehat{=}} QueryForIn1 \land Success$$

$$RQueryForOut1 \mathrel{\widehat{=}} QueryForOut1 \land Success$$

$$RQueryForUsers1 \mathrel{\widehat{=}} QueryForUsers1 \land Success$$

There is no need for any error-handling schemas because none of these querying operations has preconditions. The refined querying operations can easily be specified as follows.

```
┌─QueryForIn1──────────────────
│ ΞState
│ in1! : ℙ STAFF_ID
├──────────────────────
│ in1! = in1
└──────────────────────────────
```

```
┌─QueryForOut1─────────────────
│ ΞState
│ out1! : ℙ STAFF_ID
├──────────────────────
│ out1! = out1
└──────────────────────────────
```

```
┌─QueryForUsers1───────────────
│ ΞState
│ users1! : ℙ STAFF_ID
├──────────────────────
│ users1! = users1
└──────────────────────────────
```

9.7 IMPLEMENTING THE REFINED SPECIFICATION IN CODE

The first refinement produced is, in fact, sufficiently well developed to be written in code. The code used is a Pascal-like pseudocode. The infinite arrays have been implemented as finite ones, and the maximum array size has been chosen arbitrarily to be 200. The system is therefore being relied upon to warn us if any array variables are out of bounds!

At the highest level the implementation is a menu of possible operations from which the user makes a selection. When the program is run the system is initialised, as in *InitState1*, and then the menu of possible operations is displayed. Implementation details such as these are seldom specified, but can easily be effected. The implementation at the highest level is thus as follows.

```
Program SecuritySystem
var    in, out, users : array[1..200] of STAFF_ID
       count : INTEGER
       x, y, z : INTEGER
       menunum : 1..8
begin
       set x, y, z to 0
       set count to 1
       while count ≤ 200 do
```

```
                begin
                set in[count] to null_id
                set out[count] to null_id
                set users[count] to null_id
                set count to count + 1
        end
        do MenuPrint
        read menunum
        while menunum ≠ 1 do
                begin
                do Option(menunum)
                do MenuPrint
                read menunum
        end
end
```

The *MenuPrint* and *Option* procedures are as follows.

```
Procedure MenuPrint
begin
        write "enter 1 for Quit"
        write "enter 2 for Add"
        write "enter 3 for CheckIn"
        write "enter 4 for CheckOut"
        write "enter 5 for Remove"
        write "enter 6 for QueryForIn"
        write "enter 7 for QueryForOut"
        write "enter 8 for QueryForUsers"
end

Procedure Option(menunum : 2..8)
begin
        case menunum of
                2 then do RAdd
                3 then do RCheckIn
                4 then do RCheckOut
                5 then do RRemove
                6 then do RQueryForIn
                7 then do RQueryForOut
                8 then do RQueryForUsers
        end
end
```

Next we define the reporting procedures that are part of the robust user interfaces. These procedures are simple **write** statements as follows.

```
Procedure Success
begin
      write "operation carried out successfully"
end

Procedure AlreadyUser
begin
      write "person is already a user"
end

Procedure StaffIn
begin
      write "person is already in the building"
end

Procedure NotUser
begin
      write "person is not known"
end

Procedure StaffOut
begin
      write "person is already outside the building"
end

Procedure StillIn
begin
      write "person is still in the building"
end
```

The next set of procedures define the successful operations namely *Add*, *CheckIn*, *CheckOut* and *Remove*. Note that they mirror very closely the refined schemas that specify their operation.

```
Procedure Add(new : STAFF_ID)
begin
      set y to y + 1
      set out[y] to new
      set z to z + 1
      set users[z] to new
end

Procedure CheckIn(j : 1..200)
begin
      set x to x + 1
      set in[x] to out[j]
      set y to y - 1
      set out[j] to out[y + 1]
      set out[y + 1] to null_id
end
```

```
Procedure CheckOut(i : 1..200)
begin
      set y to y + 1
      set out[y] to in[i]
      set x to x - 1
      set in[i] to in[x + 1]
      set in[x + 1] to null_id
end

Procedure Remove(j,k : 1..200)
begin
      set y to y - 1
      set out[j] to out[y + 1]
      set out[y + 1] to null_id
      set z to z - 1
      set users[k] to users[z + 1]
      set users[z + 1] to null_id
end
```

We now tackle the problem of giving the coding for the robust operations which call the procedures we have just defined. The coding is fairly straightforward, and centres on providing the necessary information for an **if_then_else** implementation along the lines of

if *condition* **then do** *Op* **else do** *OpError*

The robust *Add* operation is thus implemented by the following procedure.

```
Procedure RAdd
var k : 1..200 ; new : STAFF_ID
begin
      write "please enter staff_id"
      read new
      set k to 1
      while users[k] ≠ new ∧ k ≤ z do
      begin
            set k to k + 1
      end
      if k < z then
      begin
            do Add(new)
            do Success
      else
            do AlreadyUser
      end
end
```

The procedure works as follows. First, using the **while–do** construct whether or not *new* is a user is checked. If this checking reveals that *new* is not a user then *Add* is carried out, otherwise *AlreadyUser* is executed. The checking is simply done by comparing whether the array index *k* exceeds the high–water mark *z*.

The robust *CheckIn* procedure is coded as follows.

```
Procedure RCheckIn
var j : 1..200 ; staff : STAFF_ID ; k : 1..200
begin
        write "please enter staff_id"
        read staff
        set j to 1
        set k to 1
        while out[j] ≠ staff ∧ j ≤ y do
        begin
                set j to j + 1
        end
        while users[k] ≠ staff ∧ k ≤ z do
        begin
                set k to k + 1
        end
        if j ≤ y then
        begin
                do CheckIn(j)
                do Success
        else
                if k ≤ z then
                begin
                        do StaffIn
                else
                        do NotUser
                end
        end
end
```

The two **while–do** loops establish whether or not the input *staff* is in *out* or in *users*, and the **if_then_else** construct does the rest.

The robust *CheckOut* operation is coded in a very similar way as follows.

```
Procedure RCheckOut
var i : 1..200 ; staff : STAFF_ID ; k : 1..200
begin
        write "please enter staff_id"
        read staff
        set i to 1
```

```
        set k to 1
        while in[i] ≠ staff ∧ i ≤ x do
        begin
              set i to i + 1
        end
        while users[k] ≠ staff ∧ k ≤ z do
        begin
              set k to k + 1
        end
        if i ≤ x then
        begin
              do CheckOut(i)
              do Success
        else
              if k ≤ z then
              begin
                    do StaffOut
              else
                    do NotUser
              end
        end
  end
```

The robust *Remove* procedure is as follows.

```
  Procedure RRemove
  var j : 1..200 ; staff : STAFF_ID ; k : 1..200
  begin
        write "please enter staff_id"
        read staff
        set j to 1
        set k to 1
        while out[j] ≠ staff ∧ j ≤ y do
        begin
              set j to j + 1
        end
        while users[k] ≠ staff ∧ k ≤ z do
        begin
              set k to k + 1
        end
        if j ≤ y then
        begin
              do Remove(j,k)
              do Success
        else
              if k ≤ z then
              begin
```

```
                do StillIn
        else
                do NotUser
        end
    end
end
```

All that remains to complete the implementation is to code the robust querying operations. These may be coded in a straightforward way and are left to the reader as an exercise.

9.8 SUMMARY AND OBSERVATIONS

All the details of implementing specifications are really too numerous to be covered by looking at just one example. However, the example considered is typical of many systems, and it is worth summarising the general points that emerge.

First of all, with regard to refinement and coding, we note the following key stages.

- Choose a concrete data structure.

- Specify the new system state in terms of this concrete data structure.

- Relate the state variables in the new system state to the state variables in the original abstract state, via an appropriate abstraction relation.

- Specify the new initial state of the system.

- Refine the rest of the specification.

- Repeat all of this (if necessary) until the refined specification is sufficiently well developed to produce the coding.

- Think of the highest level interface that needs to be supplied and write it.

- Implement the schemas to produce the complete robust system.

Secondly, with respect to structure, it is worth noting that the overall structure of an implementation is the same as that of the specification. Schemas become procedures, almost one for one, and a program can be built up by implementing the specification piecemeal, a schema at a time.

This approach not only makes the task of building the coding much easier but, importantly, it also simplifies the problem of verifying that the resulting coding is correct. To show that a program is correct all that must be done is to demonstrate that each procedure correctly implements the schema from whence it came. Demonstrating that a procedure correctly implements the schema requires a formal proof. In the next chapter we consider the mathematics of proof, and the rules that underpin the processes of inference and logical deduction.

9.9 EXERCISES

1. As an exercise in coding a specification try writing the coding for the following procedures relating to the simple security system.
   (i) *RQueryForIn*
   (ii) *RQueryForOut*
   (iii) *RQueryForUsers*

2. Refine the specification of the simple telephone directory system that was considered in the worked examples of Chapter 4. Represent the directory function *dir* by two arrays as follows.

   names : **array**[1..100] **of** *NAME*
   numbers : **array**[1..100] **of** $\mathbb{N}$

3. Try coding up the refined specification of the telephone directory system in pseudocode.

4. Refine and implement the specification for the simple banking system that was considered in the worked examples of Chapter 5.

CHAPTER 10

The role of proof

10.1 INTRODUCTION

To develop software rigorously we use mathematics; mathematics enables us to reason formally. Ideally, when building a specification, theorems and proof should be used to demonstrate that the specification is self-consistent and complete. Similarly, when refining a specification, we should demonstrate rigorously, via proof, that each refinement is consistent with the first abstract specification. We should also show rigorously that the coding implements the specification.

All this means that it is necessary to know something about proof and about the kind of proofs that must be carried out in developing software rigorously. This chapter looks at proof, at how to check a specification for consistency, at refinement proofs, and at program proving.

10.2 THE NOTION OF VALIDITY AND PROOF

Consider the following line of reasoning.

- If the number of days a book is overdue exceeds 7, a reminder is issued.

- No reminder has been issued.

- Therefore the number of days overdue is 7 or less.

This is an example of a logical argument. It contains two statements called premises, which are the first two statements, and a third statement which is the conclusion. Analysing the reasoning we see that there is no disputing the validity of the argument. If the premises are true, then logic forces us to accept the conclusion. This is an example of a valid argument.

In mathematics we define a valid argument as follows.

- A valid argument is a finite set of statements P_1, P_2, ..., P_n called premises, together with a statement C called the conclusion, such that the implication statement $P_1 \wedge P_2 \wedge \ldots \wedge P_n \Rightarrow C$ is true.

Thus an argument is valid if, whenever each of its premises is true, its conclusion is true.

To signify a valid argument we write

$$P_1, P_2, \ldots, P_n \vDash C$$

or equivalently

$$\vDash P_1 \wedge P_2 \wedge \ldots \wedge P_n \Rightarrow C$$

The symbol $\vDash$ is called the semantic turnstile. The first expression means that P_1, P_2, ..., P_n being true forces C to be true. The second expression means that the statement $P_1 \wedge P_2 \wedge \ldots \wedge P_n \Rightarrow C$ must necessarily be true. Roughly speaking, the $\vDash$ symbol means "it is obvious that".

Consider, now, another logical argument.

- x is an odd number.

- y is an odd number.

- Therefore the product $x*y$ is also an odd number.

In contrast to our first example, it is not so obvious why the conclusion here should be correct. The premises do not logically force the conclusion. The conclusion is correct, but the fact that it follows from the premises needs to be demonstrated. We say that the conclusion requires to be proved.

To signify that a conclusion C can be proved to follow from premises P_1, P_2, ..., P_n we write

$$P_1, P_2, \ldots, P_n \vdash C$$

or equivalently

$$\vdash P_1 \wedge P_2 \wedge \ldots \wedge P_n \Rightarrow C$$

The $\vdash$ symbol is known as the syntactic turnstile and each of the expressions is called a theorem. A theorem can be defined as follows.

- A theorem consists of a finite set of statements $P_1, P_2, \ldots, P_n$ called premises, together with a statement C called a conclusion, such that the conclusion can be shown to follow from the premises in a finite number of valid steps.

A valid step is any step that comes about through the application of a valid argument; deriving a required conclusion from given premises, in a finite number of valid steps, is known as giving a proof. A proof is nothing more than a finite sequence of statements, the last of which is the required conclusion. It can therefore be written down as follows.

$$< S_1, S_2, \ldots, S_i, \ldots, C >$$

Each successive statement must necessarily satisfy the following condition.

$$S_1, S_2, \ldots, S_{i-1} \models S_i$$

To give a proof it is generally accepted that this last condition will be satisfied if one of the following occurs.

- S_i is one of the premises of the theorem
- $\models S_i$
- S_i follows from $S_1, S_2, \ldots, S_{i-1}$ by an inference rule (considered below)
- S_i is logically equivalent to one of the statements $S_1, S_2, \ldots, S_{i-1}$

10.3 INFERENCE RULES

Much work has been carried out to mechanise the operation of giving a proof, so that computers might eventually prove theorems for us. Several prototype theorem provers exist, and they work by rewriting expressions until the required conclusion appears. The rewrite rules are based on inference rules which are classified as elimination rules or introduction rules. The quantities being eliminated and introduced are the logical connectives and quantifiers, namely $\wedge$, $\vee$, $\Rightarrow$, $\neg$, $\forall$ and $\exists$.

Elimination rules

The following six rules are called elimination rules because a symbol, which appeared in one of the premises, is absent from the conclusion.

1. $\wedge E : P \wedge Q \models P$

   This is the simplification or specialisation rule; $\wedge$ E stands for "and" elimination. If we accept that the statement $P \wedge Q$ is true, then it is valid to infer that the statement P is true.

2. $\vee$ E : $P \vee Q,\ P \Rightarrow R,\ Q \Rightarrow R \models R$

   This rule is often called the law of reduction of cases. It states that, if the statement $P \vee Q$ is true and that both P and Q imply R, it is valid to infer that the statement R is true.

3. $\Rightarrow$ E : $P,\ P \Rightarrow Q \models Q$

   This is the modus ponens rule. It states that, if P and $P \Rightarrow Q$ are both true, it is valid to infer that Q is true.

4. $\neg$ E : $\neg P \vdash F \models P$

   This is the proof by contradiction rule. It states that, if the assumption that P is false can be shown to lead to a contradiction, it is valid to assume P is true. Here F stands for the truth value *false*.

5. $\forall$ E : $\forall\ x : X \bullet P(x) \models P(c) \wedge c \in X$

   This is the universal instantiation rule. It states that, if $P(x)$ is true for all x in the set X, it is valid to infer that $P(c)$ is true for any particular element c in X.

6. $\exists$ E : $\exists\ x : X \bullet P(x) \models P(c) \wedge c \in X$

   This is the existential instantiation rule. This states that, if we accept that there exists an x in the set X for which $P(x)$ holds, it is valid to infer that $P(c)$ is true for some particular element c in X.

Introduction rules

Note that in these introduction rules a symbol, which does not appear in the premises, is introduced into the conclusion.

1. $\wedge$ I : $P,\ Q \models P \wedge Q$

   This rule is called the conjunction rule; $\wedge$ I stands for "and" introduction. It states that, if each of P and Q is true, it is valid to claim that the statement $P \wedge Q$ is true.

2. $\vee$ I : $P \models P \vee Q$

   This is the addition rule. It simply states, that if P is true, it is valid to infer that $P \vee Q$ is true for any statement Q.

3. $\Rightarrow \text{I} : P \vdash Q \models P \Rightarrow Q$

   This rule states that, if we can prove that Q follows from P, it is valid to assume that the statement $P \Rightarrow Q$ is true.

4. $\neg \text{I} : P \vdash F \models \neg P$

   This is the proof by contradiction rule in disguise. If we can show that assuming P is true leads to a contradiction, then it is valid to assume that $\neg P$ will be true.

5. $\forall \text{I} : P(c) \wedge c \in X \models \forall x : X \bullet P(x)$

   This is the universal generalisation rule. It must be used with extreme care. It states that if, for an arbitrary member c from the set X, we can show that $P(c)$ is true without making use of any property of c other than the fact that c belongs to X, then it is valid to infer that $P(x)$ is true regardless of the value of x.

6. $\exists \text{I} : P(c) \wedge c \in X \models \exists x : X \bullet P(x)$

   This rule, known as the rule of existential generalisation, states that if we can show that property P holds for an element c, belonging to a set X, then it is valid to assume that there exists an element x in X for which $P(x)$ is true.

10.4 LOGICAL EQUIVALENCES

Rarely in a proof can we establish the validity of a conclusion by using inference rules alone. More often than not we have to make use of other theorems and definitions and, in particular, various logical equivalences. We have already used the equivalence connective and noted that, if P and Q are equivalent, this means that $P \Rightarrow Q$ and $Q \Rightarrow P$ are true. As far as valid arguments go this means that if $P \Leftrightarrow Q$ is true then

$$P \models Q \text{ and } Q \models P$$

In other words it is valid, when giving a proof, to use any statement that is equivalent to any preceding statement to enable the proof to be established.

There is a wealth of logical equivalences we can use in theorem proving. Typical equivalences that are useful are DeMorgan's laws

$$\neg(A \vee B) \Leftrightarrow \neg A \wedge \neg B$$

$$\neg(A \wedge B) \Leftrightarrow \neg A \vee \neg B$$

and the alternative expression for $A \Rightarrow B$ in terms of the $\neg$ and $\vee$ connectives, namely

$$A \Rightarrow B \Leftrightarrow \neg A \vee B$$

The list of useful equivalences is as long as we care to make it. The following equivalences, involving the quantifiers $\forall$ and $\exists$, are worth noting.

1. $\neg(\forall\ x : X \bullet P(x)) \Leftrightarrow \exists\ x : X \bullet \neg P(x)$

2. $\neg(\exists\ x : X \bullet P(x)) \Leftrightarrow \forall\ x : X \bullet \neg P(x)$

3. $\forall\ x : X \bullet (P(x) \wedge Q(x)) \Leftrightarrow \forall\ x : X \bullet P(x) \wedge \forall\ x : X \bullet Q(x)$

4. $\exists\ x : X \bullet (P(x) \vee Q(x)) \Leftrightarrow \exists\ x : X \bullet P(x) \vee \exists\ x : X \bullet Q(x)$

5. $\forall\ x : X \bullet (P(x) \wedge Q(y)) \Leftrightarrow (\forall\ x : X \bullet P(x)) \wedge Q(y)$

6. $\forall\ x : X \bullet (P(x) \vee Q(y)) \Leftrightarrow (\forall\ x : X \bullet P(x)) \vee Q(y)$

7. $\exists\ x : X \bullet (P(x) \wedge Q(y)) \Leftrightarrow (\exists\ x : X \bullet P(x)) \wedge Q(y)$

8. $\exists\ x : X \bullet (P(x) \vee Q(y)) \Leftrightarrow (\exists\ x : X \bullet P(x)) \vee Q(y)$

10.5 MATHEMATICAL INDUCTION

In addition to using inference rules, or logical equivalences, we may have need to make use of mathematical induction to supply a proof. Proof by induction is useful to establish the validity of some property defined over the natural numbers. We might have to show, for example, that the sum $S(n)$ of the natural numbers 0, 1, ..., n is given by the formula $n(n+1)/2$. In other words, to show that some property $P(n)$ holds for all n.

Proof by induction works by establishing first the base case, namely that $P(0)$ is true, and then showing that $P(k) \vdash P(k+1)$ follows for arbitrary k. If we can establish these two steps, then it follows that $P(n)$ is true for all n.

Such proofs by induction are commonplace in software engineering when reasoning about a recursive definition, or about the correctness or otherwise of a programming construct such as a **while–do** loop, for example.

10.6 SETTING OUT A PROOF

When giving a proof, we should set out the proof in such a way to reveal the valid reasoning behind our proof. To demonstrate how we set out a proof formally, suppose we wish to establish the validity of the following very simple theorem.

$$x > 0,\ (x > 0) \Rightarrow (x \in \text{dom } f),\ (x \in \text{dom } f) \Rightarrow f(x) \in A \vdash f(x) \in A$$

The proof can be set out formally as shown below. It is normal to state the theorem to be proved first and then list the statements that logically lead to the conclusion, with brief explanations of why each step is valid.

$x > 0,\ (x > 0) \Rightarrow (x \in \text{dom } f),\ (x \in \text{dom } f) \Rightarrow f(x) \in A \vdash f(x) \in A$

1	$x > 0$	premise
2	$(x > 0) \Rightarrow (x \in \text{dom } f)$	premise
3	$(x \in \text{dom } f) \Rightarrow f(x) \in A$	premise
4	$x \in \text{dom } f$	from 1, 2 by $\Rightarrow$ E
5	$f(x) \in A$	from 3, 4 by $\Rightarrow$ E
	QED	

Statements 1, 2 and 3 are premises, which we assume are true. Statement 4 follows from statements 1 and 2 via modus ponens. Similarly statement 5 follows from statements 3 and 4 by the same inference rule. Statement 5 is the conclusion statement of our theorem and we signify that our theorem has been proved by writing QED.

The example considered is clearly a very simple one, and the proof is quite short. More generally, formal proofs are longer than this, as our next example shows. Although the problem is intrinsically a simple one, the need to develop the proof in a series of valid steps means that the proof can become quite lengthy. The problem considered is the proof that, if x is an odd number and y is an odd number, the product $x*y$ is also an odd number. The series of statements, together with each valid argument, is as follows.

x is odd, y is odd $\vdash$ $x*y$ is odd

1	x is odd	premise
2	y is odd	premise
3	$\forall z : \mathbb{Z} \bullet z \text{ is odd} \Leftrightarrow$ $\exists n : \mathbb{Z} \bullet z = 2*n + 1$	definition
4	$x \text{ is odd} \Leftrightarrow \exists n : \mathbb{Z} \bullet x = 2*n + 1$	from 3 by $\forall$ E

5	$\exists\ n : \mathbb{Z} \bullet x = 2*n + 1$	from 1 and 4
6	$x = 2*p + 1$	from 5 by $\exists$ E
7	y is odd $\Leftrightarrow \exists\ n : \mathbb{Z} \bullet y = 2*n + 1$	from 3 by $\forall$ E
8	$\exists\ n : \mathbb{Z} \bullet y = 2*n + 1$	from 2 and 7
9	$y = 2*q + 1$	from 8 by $\exists$ E
10	$x*y = (2*p + 1)*(2*q + 1)$	from 6 and 9
11	$(2*p + 1)*(2*q + 1)$ $= 2*(2*p*q + p + q) + 1$	algebra of * and +
12	$x*y = 2*(2*p*q + p + q)$	from 10 and 11
13	$2*p*q + p + q \in \mathbb{Z}$	property of integers
14	$\exists\ n : \mathbb{Z} \bullet x*y = 2*n + 1$	from 12, 13 by $\exists$ I
15	$x*y$ is odd $\Leftrightarrow \exists\ n : \mathbb{Z} \bullet x*y = 2*n + 1$	from 3 by $\forall$ E
16	$x*y$ is odd	from 14 and 15

QED

We see that the proof is indeed rather lengthy for what is really a simple theorem. This is because we have set out the proof formally, and included every step needed to take us rigorously from the premises to the conclusion. Some formal proofs can be extremely long affairs. When reliable theorem provers are finally available this will not matter. However, while theorems continue to be proved by hand, not surprisingly there is the temptation to take for granted some of the more tedious steps and group together several others in order to shorten the proof. If we do this, the formal proof becomes an informal one, which is often easier to read. The above proof, for example, could be set out informally as follows.

x is odd, y is odd $\vdash x*y$ is odd

---

1 x and y being odd implies that x is of the form $2*p + 1$ and y is of the form $2*q + 1$, where p and q belong to $\mathbb{Z}$

2 $x*y$ is therefore $(2*p + 1)*(2*q + 1)$, ie $2*(2*p*q + p + q) + 1$, which in turn is of the form $2*n + 1$ where n belongs to $\mathbb{Z}$

3 $x*y$ is therefore an odd number

QED

The proof is just as valid as an argument, though much more informal.

Clearly, too much informality has the danger of allowing errors and inconsistencies to creep into a proof; having a formal and rigorous approach to fall back on has its advantages. In what follows, however, when checking the consistency of specifictions, refinements, and the correctness of coding, we appeal mainly to informal proofs to establish the required theorems.

10.7 CHECKING THE CONSISTENCY OF SPECIFICATIONS

At the beginning of Chapter 9 the point was made that before a specification is turned into coding we ought to satisfy ourselves that it really is for the system that the customer wants. Validating a system is not easy, but having a formal specification available greatly facilitates the process. Establishing that a system possesses certain desirable properties can be accomplished by setting up the properties as theorems to be proved, and then bringing to bear on the problem all the power of valid reasoning. Being able to reason about the system at the specification stage, when changes can still be incorporated, has its advantages.

The kind of issues that need to be addressed about any specification are the following.

- Do state variables actually exist that satisfy the data invariant set down in the state schema? If examples cannot be found, then the system can never be set up.

- Do operations we have specified work as they should? Does an operation precondition really guarantee the outputs and final states that are required, and is the data invariant preserved by the operation?

- Does one operation that is specifically meant to undo the effect of another really work like that, and so on?

All these questions, and more, must be answered to the satisfaction of all concerned before implementation takes place. If all the properties can be proved to hold, then we can be confident that the system we have built is at least internally consistent, and appears to work as it should.

To put all this into the context of theorem proving it is best to consider an example. For simplicity let us look at the simple security system that we considered in Chapter 3, and concentrate on the state schema together with the *CheckIn* and *CheckOut* operations. Let us demonstrate, via proof, that the following properties hold.

- Values for the state variables can be found which satisfy the data invariant in the state schema.

- The *CheckIn* operation works as we expect; in other words, the precondition of *CheckIn* is sufficient to guarantee the existence of the required after states, and these satisfy the data invariant.

- *CheckIn* followed by *CheckOut*, when the same staff member is involved, constitutes a null operation.

To show that a state exists that satisfies the data invariant we need to prove that there exists values of *in*, *out* and *users* that satisfy the predicates of the *State* schema. This requirement can be expressed as a theorem to be proved as follows.

$$\vdash \exists\ in, out, users : \mathbb{P}\ STAFF\_ID \bullet State$$

The proof follows by furnishing suitable values for *in*, *out* and *users* and checking that they satisfy the data invariant.

$\vdash \exists\ in, out, users : \mathbb{P}\ STAFF\_ID \bullet State$

---

1 Let *users* be any set of staff identity values, A

2 Let *in* be the empty set of identity values, $\emptyset$

3 Let *out* be the set A

4 *in*, *out* and *users* are of type $\mathbb{P}\ STAFF\_ID$

5 $in \cap out = \emptyset \cap A = \emptyset$

6 $in \cup out = \emptyset \cup A = A = users$

7 $\exists\ in, out, users : \mathbb{P}\ STAFF\_ID \bullet in \cap out = \emptyset \land$
$in \cup out = users$

8 $\exists\ in, out, users : \mathbb{P}\ STAFF\_ID \bullet State$

QED

To prove the second requirement, that the *CheckIn* operation works as it should, we check that the precondition for *CheckIn*, namely $staff? \in out$, is sufficient to guarantee a final state of the system having the requisite properties set down in the *CheckIn* schema. As a theorem we write this requirement as follows.

$$[State\ ;\ staff? : STAFF\_ID \mid staff? \in out] \vdash \exists\ State' \bullet CheckIn$$

The construct in the premise, which has the form

[declarations | predicate]

is an alternative and horizontal way of writing out a schema, which is particularly useful when we wish to form a schema that does not have any obvious name.

An informal proof of the theorem is given below. We establish that a final state can be found that satisfies the predicates of the *CheckIn* schema, and which also preserves the data invariant.

$[State\ ;\ staff? : STAFF\_ID \mid staff? \in out] \vdash \exists\ State' \bullet CheckIn$

---

1 From the premise we know that $in \in \mathbb{P}\ STAFF\_ID$ and $staff? \in STAFF\_ID$

2 It follows, therefore, that $in \cup \{staff?\} \in \mathbb{P}\ STAFF\_ID$

3 Similarly, since $out \in STAFF\_ID$, it follows that $out \setminus \{staff?\} \in \mathbb{P}\ STAFF\_ID$

4 Thus, from 2 and 3 and noting that $users \in \mathbb{P}\ STAFF\_ID$, it follows that $\exists\ in', out', users' : \mathbb{P}\ STAFF\_ID \bullet$
$in' = in \cup \{staff?\} \land out' = out \setminus \{staff?\} \land users' = users$

5 From 4 we can note that

$$\begin{aligned} in' \cup out' &= (in \cup \{staff?\}) \cup (out \setminus \{staff?\}) \\ &= in \cup (\{staff?\} \cup (out \setminus \{staff?\})) \\ &= in \cup out \\ &= users \\ &= users' \end{aligned}$$

6 Also, from 4, we may note

$$\begin{aligned} in' \cap out' &= (in \cup \{staff?\}) \cap (out \setminus \{staff?\}) \\ &= (in \cap (out \setminus \{staff?\}) \cup \\ &\quad (\{staff?\} \cap (out \setminus \{staff?\})) \\ &= ((in \cap out) \setminus \{staff?\}) \cup \\ &\quad ((\{staff?\} \cap out) \setminus \{staff?\}) \\ &= (\emptyset \setminus \{staff?\}) \cup (\{staff?\} \setminus \{staff?\}) \\ &= \emptyset \cup \emptyset \\ &= \emptyset \end{aligned}$$

7 From 5 and 6 it follows that in', out', $users'$ satisfy the data invariant

8 From 7 and 4 it follows that the predicates of $\exists\ State' \bullet CheckIn$ are valid.

QED

To establish the last requirement, that *CheckIn* followed by *CheckOut* constitutes a null operation, we must show that the initial and final states of *CheckIn* ⨾ *CheckOut*, when the same staff identity code is involved, are identical. In other words we must prove the following theorem.

$$CheckIn \fatsemi CheckOut \vdash in' = in \land out' = out \land users' = users$$

This proof can be given informally as follows.

$CheckIn \; ⨾ \; CheckOut \vdash in' = in \wedge out' = out \wedge users' = users$

---

1 $staff? \in out$ (precondition for *CheckIn*)

2 $\exists\, in_0, out_0, users_0 : \mathbb{P}\, STAFF\_ID \bullet$
$in_0 = in \cup \{staff?\} \wedge in' = in_0 \setminus \{staff?\}$
$out_0 = out \setminus \{staff?\} \wedge out' = out_0 \cup \{staff?\}$
$users_0 = users \wedge users' = users_0$
(predicates of*CheckIn* ⨾ *CheckOut*)

3 From 2 it follows that
$in' = (in \cup \{staff?\}) \setminus \{staff?\}$
$= in$ (from 1)

$out' = (out \setminus \{staff?\}) \cup \{staff?\}$
$= out$ (from 1)

$users' = users$

4 From 3 it follows that $in' = in \wedge out' = out \wedge users' = users$ by the introduction of the $\wedge$ rule

QED

Having established these three results we can be confident that the schemas we have written are working in the way they should and that the specification, such as it is, captures the requirements of a security system in a way that is internally consistent.

Before we look at refinement proofs, it is worth noting one important aspect of the role of proof in software specification. Proofs are not something supplied to give the final seal of approval to a specification prior to coding the system. It is vital that we carry out proofs whilst building the specification, so that proof becomes an integral part of the whole software development process. By reasoning about what we are doing at all stages, there is far less chance of major inconsistencies propagating too far into the project. Proof, therefore, has a major role to play in ensuring both quality and cost-effectiveness in software engineering.

10.8 REFINEMENT PROOFS

Each refinement stage is meant to be more concrete than the one before. If we let the concrete stage be represented with a letter *C* and the stage immediately before it by a letter *A* (for more abstract), then the theorems that must be proved about refinement, that apply for each operation we have specified, are the following.

- pre(Aop) $\wedge$ $Abs \vdash$ pre(Cop)

- $\text{pre}(Aop) \wedge Abs \wedge Cop \vdash \exists\ AState' \bullet Abs' \wedge Aop$

The theorems tell us that

- if the precondition for the abstract operation is satisfied, then this together with the abstraction relation should guarantee that the precondition for the concrete operation is satisfied

- if the precondition for the abstract operation is satisfied then the concrete operation, when performed, should guarantee the existence of an abstract final state satisfying both *Abs'* and the predicates in *Aop*.

Again, a simple example is needed to see how such theorems are proved.

Consider the refinement of the security system and, in particular, let us check that the *Add1* schema is a consistent refinement of the abstract *Add* schema. The first theorem can thus be expressed as

$$\text{pre}(Add) \wedge Abs \vdash \text{pre}(Add1)$$

The proof is fairly straightforward and can be given informally as follows.

$\text{pre}(Add) \wedge Abs \vdash \text{pre}(Add1)$

---

1 $\text{pre}(Add)$ is $new? \notin users$

2 The relevant predicate from *Abs* that we need is
$users = \{k : 1..z \bullet users1(k)\}$

3 From 1 and 2 it follows that
$new? \notin \{k : 1..z \bullet users1(k)\}$

4 Thus $\forall\ k : 1..z \bullet users1(k) \neq new?$

5 This is the precondition for *Add1*

QED

The second theorem can be expressed as

$$\text{pre}(Add) \wedge Abs \wedge Add1 \vdash \exists\ State' \bullet Abs' \wedge Add$$

It must be shown that the premise implies the existence of *in'*, *out'* and *users'* that satisfy *Abs'* and the predicates of *Add*.

The proof is as follows.

$\text{pre}(Add) \wedge Abs \wedge Add1 \vdash \exists\ State' \bullet Abs' \wedge Add$

---

1 $new? \in users$ is the precondition for Add

2 The Abs predicates are
$in = \{i : 1..x \bullet in1(i)\}$
$out = \{j : 1..y \bullet out1(j)\}$
$users = \{k : 1..z \bullet users1(k)\}$

3 The relevant $Add1$ predicates are
$in1' = in1$
$x' = x$
$y' = y + 1$
$out1' = out1 \oplus \{y' \mapsto new?\}$
$z' = z + 1$
$users1' = users1 \oplus \{z' \mapsto new?\}$

4 $in' = \{i : 1..x' \bullet in1'(i)\}$ from 2
$= \{i : 1..x \bullet in1(i)\}$ from 3
$= in$ from 2

5 $out' = \{j : 1..y' \bullet out1'(j)\}$ from 2
$= \{j : 1..y + 1 \bullet out1'(j)\}$ from 3
$= \{j : 1..y \bullet out1'(j)\} \cup \{new?\}$
$= \{j : 1..y \bullet out1(j)\} \cup \{new?\}$ from 3
$= out \cup \{new?\}$ from 2

6 By the same reasoning as in 5 it follows that $users'$, as defined via 2, satisfies $users' = users \cup \{new?\}$

7 Thus $\exists\ State' \bullet Abs' \wedge Add$ is true

QED

10.9 PROGRAM PROVING

Suppose the concrete specification is again represented by a letter C and the implementation by the letter I. The theorems to be proved to establish that the coding implements the concrete specification are the following ones.

- $\text{pre}(Cop) \vdash \text{pre}(Iop)$
- $\text{pre}(Cop)$ with $Iop \vdash Cop$

These theorems require that

- if the precondition of the concrete operation is satisfied, this should guarantee that the precondition of the coding is also satisfied

- the precondition of the concrete operation together with the coding should guarantee the conditions set down in the concrete operation.

As a simple illustration consider the specification for a square root algorithm, called *CRoot*, and the corresponding program, *IRoot*, that uses the standard *sqrt* function. The specification and implementation are as follows.

```
┌─CRoot──────────────────────
│ x?, y! : ℝ
├────────────────────
│ x? ≥ 0
│ x? = y!*y!
└────────────────────────────
```

```
1   Program IRoot
2   var x?, y! : ℝ
3   begin
4         read x?
5         if x? ≥ 0 then do
6         begin
7               set y! to sqrt(x?)
8               write y!
9         else
10              write "Negative input – no root"
11        end
12  end
```

The workings of the specification and implementation are significantly different. The implementation, for example, caters for any $x?$ value of type $\mathbb{R}$, whilst the schema will only work if $x? \geq 0$. However, as we shall now show, program *IRoot* is a correct implementation of *CRoot*. We start by establishing the theorem pre(*CRoot*) $\vdash$ pre(*IRoot*). The informal proof is as follows.

pre(*CRoot*) $\vdash$ pre(*IRoot*)

---

1 pre(*CRoot*) is equivalent to the condition $x? \geq 0 \land x? \in \mathbb{R}$

2 By the $\land$ E rule in 1 it follows that $x? \in \mathbb{R}$

3 $x? \in \mathbb{R}$ is the only precondition for the coding

4 pre(*CRoot*) $\vdash$ pre(*IRoot*)

QED

We now show that pre(*CRoot*) with *IRoot* guarantees the declarations and predicates of *CRoot* by proving the theorem pre(*CRoot*) with *IRoot* $\vdash$ *CRoot*

In what follows we assume that {1 − *n*} stands for that part of *IRoot* that includes statements 1 to *n* inclusive. Also, let pre(*CRoot*){1 − *n*} stand for pre(*CRoot*) with {1 − *n*} and be the declarations and predicates that describe the state of computation after the first *n* lines of coding have been executed, given that pre(*CRoot*) was true to start with. The theorem is now proved by showing that pre(*CRoot*) with *IRoot* implies the declarations and predicates contained within the schema *CRoot*. The proof is again an informal one.

pre(*CRoot*) with *IRoot* $\vdash$ *CRoot*

---

1 pre(*CRoot*) is equivalent to $x? \in \mathbb{R} \wedge x? \geqslant 0$

2 Statements 1, 2, 3 and 4 when executed, together with pre(*CRoot*), imply $x? \in \mathbb{R} \wedge x? \geqslant 0 \wedge y! \in \mathbb{R}$

3 Since $x? \geqslant 0$, the **else** part of the implementation is never reached, so pre(*CRoot*){1 − 12} implies $x? \in \mathbb{R} \wedge y! \in \mathbb{R} \wedge x? \geqslant 0 \wedge y! = sqrt(x?)$

4 $y! = sqrt(x?)$ implies $x? = y!*y!$

5 It follows that pre(*C*){1 − 12} implies $x? \in \mathbb{R} \wedge y! \in \mathbb{R} \wedge x? \geqslant 0 \wedge x? = y!*y!$

6 Thus pre(*CRoot*) with *IRoot* $\vdash x? \in \mathbb{R} \wedge y! \in \mathbb{R} \wedge x? \geqslant 0 \wedge x? = y!*y!$

7 $x? \in \mathbb{R} \wedge y! \in \mathbb{R}$ is equivalent to the declaration $x?, y! : \mathbb{R}$ and therefore $x? \in \mathbb{R} \wedge y! \in \mathbb{R} \wedge x? \geqslant 0 \wedge x? = y!*y!$ is equivalent to the declarations and predicates of the schema *CRoot*

8 Thus pre(*CRoot*) with *IRoot* $\vdash$ *CRoot*

QED

Thus, having established these two theorems, it follows that *IRoot* is a correct implementation of *CRoot*. Even though the workings of the specification and implementation appear to be quite different, *IRoot* matches the specification given in *CRoot*.

Before considering another correctness proof, it is important to note that the proof of the theorem pre(*Cop*) with *Iop* $\vdash$ *Cop* will in general depend on the behaviour and meaning of the programming constructs used in the implementation. In the above example, and in the one considered next, the constructs used are the standard ones of top-down structured programming.

Let us have a look, then, at an implementation with a looped structure that utilises a **while_do** construct. To keep things simple, suppose we require to work out the factorial of a given number supplied as input. We met the *factorial* function in Section 4.5 of Chapter 4 where we saw *factorial n* defined as $n*(n - 1)*(n - 2)*...*2*1$. The specification *CFact* and procedural implementation *IFact*, for the *factorial* function, are given below. The specification makes use of the predefined *factorial* function which is implemented in *IFact*.

```
┌─CFact──────────────────────
│ n?, y! : ℕ
├────────────────────
│ y! = factorial n?
└────────────────────────────
```

```
 1  Program IFact
 2  var n?, y!, c : ℕ
 3  begin
 4         read n?
 5         set c to 0
 6         set y! to 1
 7         while c < n? do
 8                begin
 9                set c to c + 1
10                set y! to c * y!
11         end
12         write y!
13  end
```

The first of the two correctness proofs is straightforward, as pre(*IFact*) and pre(*CFact*) are both the same, namely that the input *n*? should be a natural number. Thus the theorem

pre(*CFact*) $\vdash$ pre(*IFact*)

follows automatically. The second correctness proof

pre(*CFact*) with *IFact* $\vdash$ *CFact*

may be set out informally as follows.

pre(*CFact*) with *IFact* $\vdash$ *CFact*

---

1. pre(*CFact*){1 − 6} implies that the following is true after statements 1 to 6 have been executed:
   $n? \in \mathbb{N} \wedge y! \in \mathbb{N} \wedge c \in \mathbb{N} \wedge c = 0 \wedge y! = 1$
2. $c = 0 \wedge y! = 1 \wedge n? \in \mathbb{N} \models c \leq n? \wedge y! = factorial\ c$. This is true because whenever the LHS is true so, too, is the RHS

3 Thus it follows that after statements 1 to 6 have been executed the following is true:
$n? \in \mathbb{N} \wedge y! \in \mathbb{N} \wedge c \in \mathbb{N} \wedge c \leq n? \wedge y! = factorial\ c$

4 Two possibilities apply: either $\neg(c < n?)$ is true or else $c < n?$ applies

5 If $\neg(c < n?)$ applies then control transfers to statement 12 and subsequently the program halts. Thus pre(*CFact*){1 – 13} implies $n? \in \mathbb{N} \wedge y! \in \mathbb{N} \wedge c \in \mathbb{N} \wedge c \leq n? \wedge \neg(c < n?) \wedge y! = factorial\ c$

6 $c \leq n? \wedge \neg(c < n?) \models c = n?$, so the predicate in 5 collapses to $n? \in \mathbb{N} \wedge y! \in \mathbb{N} \wedge y! = factorial\ n?$

7 Thus pre(*CFact*){1 – 13} $\vdash n? \in \mathbb{N} \wedge y! \in \mathbb{N} \wedge y! = factorial\ n?$
ie if $\neg(c < n?)$ is true then pre(*CFact*) with *IFact* $\vdash$ *CFact*

8 After {1 – 6} assume $c < n?$ applies so that control now passes into the **while_do** loop

9 It follows that pre(*CFact*){1 – 7} implies $n? \in \mathbb{N} \wedge y! \in \mathbb{N} \wedge c \in \mathbb{N} \wedge c < n? \wedge y! = factorial\ c$

10 pre(*CFact*){1 – 9} implies
$n? \in \mathbb{N} \wedge y! \in \mathbb{N} \wedge c \in \mathbb{N} \wedge c - 1 < n? \wedge y! = factorial(c - 1)$
(because the previous value of c is now the new value minus 1 after the assignment in line 9 of the program)

11 In similar fashion it follows that pre(*CFact*){1 – 10} implies
$n? \in \mathbb{N} \wedge y! \in \mathbb{N} \wedge c \in \mathbb{N} \wedge c - 1 < n? \wedge y!/c = factorial(c - 1)$

12 The predicate in 11 above is logically equivalent to
$n? \in \mathbb{N} \wedge y! \in \mathbb{N} \wedge c \in \mathbb{N} \wedge c \leq n? \wedge y! = factorial\ c$

13 Thus the **while_do** loop preserves the invariant
$n? \in \mathbb{N} \wedge y! \in \mathbb{N} \wedge c \in \mathbb{N} \wedge c \leq n? \wedge y! = factorial\ c$
which applies after each cycle through the loop

14 As c increases each time through the loop, there will come a time when $\neg(c < n?)$ is true and control will transfer to statement 12, after which the program halts

15 By the reasoning used above in 5 and 6 we can thus conclude that, if $c < n?$ is true after {1 – 6}, it still follows that pre(*CFact*) with *IFact* $\vdash$ *CFact*

16 Thus from 7 and 15, using the law of reduction of cases, it follows that pre(*CFact*) with *IFact* $\vdash$ *CFact*

QED

Note that the proof depends on knowing how to deal with assignments of the form **set** c **to** $c + 1$ or **set** $y!$ **to** $c*y!$, and on having a clear knowledge of the **while_do** construct. It also depends on being able to anticipate what the "loop invariant" in the **while_do** construct is likely to be, which was necessary before we could accomplish step 2 of the proof (the base part of the induction). Once we realise that $c \leq n? \wedge y! = factorial\ c$ is unchanged by the action of the loop statements (the inductive step), the proof is relatively easy. Giving a correctness proof, therefore, not only relies on a sound knowledge of proof concepts and the notion of validity, but it also relies on an excellent grasp of programming and algorithm design.

Clearly the proof in our second example is becoming lengthy. This is due to the added complexity that arises because of the looped structure of *IFact*. However, since recursive structures nearly always result in looped procedural implementations, lengthy proofs, involving induction are not uncommon. Hence, program proving is sometimes viewed as a tedious activity by software engineers. Most would agree, though, that giving a proof is an excellent way of revealing any implementation errors. Provided informal correctness proofs are given hand-in-glove with the step-by-step implementation of a specification, the whole development process from specification to code remains manageable. It is far better to supply proofs piecemeal, as the coding is being developed, than to try and carry out a mammoth proof once the implementation is finally complete. The aim must always be to build correctness into the software as it is being developed, and maintain quality in that way, rather than debugging the software after the system has been built.

CHAPTER 11

More examples of specifications

11.1 INTRODUCTION

In this penultimate chapter we conclude our study of the mathematics of software construction by considering three more examples of specifications. The examples considered are drawn from three contrasting areas. The first area is that of mathematics itself, and we specify the problem of solving a quadratic equation. Quadratic equations are familiar to most of us and their mathematics is relatively easy. However, writing a robust specification to address all the different cases that can arise when solving a quadratic is an interesting and non–trivial exercise. The second area chosen concerns data communication over a local area network, and the problem of specifying an electronic mail system. Our third example is drawn from the rich arena of logic puzzles. We look at a particular problem, and how to specify its solution in sufficient detail so that writing a program to solve the puzzle is a fairly easy task in a language such a PROLOG.

11.2 AN EXAMPLE FROM MATHEMATICS

A quadratic equation involving a variable x is an equation of the form

$$a*x*x + b*x + c = 0$$

where * indicates scalar multiplication. The quantities a, b and c are known as the coefficients of the quadratic and they may each assume any real value. To solve the quadratic we have to find the x values that satisfy the equation. These x values are known as the roots of the quadratic. For example, the two values $x = 2$ and $x = 3$ are roots of the equation $2*x*x - 10*x + 12 = 0$.

The theory of quadratics tells us that the roots of the equation $a*x*x + b*x + c = 0$ are the two x values given by the formula

$$x = (- b \pm sqrt(b*b - 4*a*c))/(2*a)$$

This formula looks harmless enough, but problems do arise when using it. Any program that solves a quadratic must, for example, be able to cope with the following cases.

- $b*b - 4*a*c < 0$
  The formula for the roots cannot now be used because negative real numbers are not in the domain of the *sqrt* function.

- $a = 0$
  Again the formula cannot be used because division by the number zero is not permitted.

Clearly, the problem of specifying how to solve a quadratic is more complicated than the problem of simply specifying the requirements of the solution.

Developing the specification
To develop the specification we begin by parachuting in the set of real numbers as follows

$[\mathbb{R}]$

and define a free type called *MESSAGE* with the following elements

MESSAGE ::= *two_roots* | *equal_roots* | *complex_roots* |
linear_equation | *inconsistent_equation* |
degenerate_case

The need for these particular messages will become clear once we begin to build the specification.

The first important point to note is that the problem of solving a quadratic is one that involves only inputs and outputs. No state variables are needed and therefore there is no state schema to specify. The operation schemas we write thus tell us how to form the roots in terms of the coefficients of the quadratic that are supplied as inputs.

Obtaining two distinct roots
We begin, therefore, by specifying the conditions that must be met for the roots of the quadratic to be two real and distinct numbers. The following *TwoRoots* schema specifies these conditions, forms the two roots, and indicates how they are to be output along with an appropriate message.

```
┌─TwoRoots──────────────────────────────
│ a?, b?, c? : ℝ
│ output! : MESSAGE × seq ℝ
├───────────────────────────
│ a? ≠ 0
│ b?*b? - 4*a?*c? > 0
│ ∃ x1,x2 : ℝ ; message : MESSAGE •
│ x1 = (-b? + sqrt(b?*b? - 4*a?*c?))/(2*a?)
│ x2 = (-b? - sqrt(b?*b? - 4*a?*c?))/(2*a?)
│ message = two_roots
│ output! = (message, < x1,x2 >)
└──────────────────────────────────────
```

The inputs to the operation are the coefficients of the quadratic, and the output is a message followed by a sequence of real numbers which, in this case, will be the two roots. The preconditions guarantee that the two roots x_1 and x_2, as defined, will be real and distinct, and this is signified by the value of *message* that is output.

The roots are output as a sequence because the number of roots varies depending on the values of the coefficients. Using a sequence means that the part of *output*! which refers to the roots will always be of the same form.

Obtaining equal roots

The *EqualRoots* schema caters for the case of two equal roots and is given as follows.

```
┌─EqualRoots────────────────────────────
│ a?, b?, c? : ℝ
│ output! : MESSAGE × seq ℝ
├───────────────────────────
│ a? ≠ 0
│ b?*b? - 4*a?*c? = 0
│ ∃ x : ℝ ; message : MESSAGE •
│ x = -b?/(2*a?)
│ message = equal_roots
│ output! = (message, < x >)
└──────────────────────────────────────
```

Whenever $b?*b? - 4*a?*c? = 0$ and $a?$ is non–zero, the two x values in the formula for the roots are both equal to $-b?/(2*a?)$; this is the value assigned to x in the schema.

Catering for complex roots

If the value of $b?*b? - 4*a?*c?$ is negative, then no real–valued roots exist because the domain of *sqrt* does not include negative real numbers. The roots are said to be complex numbers, and the following

ComplexRoots schema caters for this particular case. Note that the number of real roots shown is zero, and an empty sequence is output together with an appropriate *complex_roots* message.

```
┌─ComplexRoots──────────────────────────
│ a?, b?, c? : ℝ
│ output! : MESSAGE × seq ℝ
├───────────────────────────────
│ b?*b? - 4*a?*c? < 0
│ ∃ message : MESSAGE •
│ message = complex_roots
│ output! = (message, < >)
└───────────────────────────────────────
```

The above schemas describe the three cases we normally expect to have to deal with when solving a quadratic. We can therefore define a schema called *QuadraticCases* as

$$QuadraticCases \triangleq TwoRoots \vee EqualRoots \vee ComplexRoots$$

which will apply in all situations where *a*? is non–zero.

Catering for special cases

If *a*? is zero, then there is not a quadratic equation to solve. However, if the value of *b*? is non–zero, the quadratic equation reduces to a linear equation given by *b*?**x* + *c*? = 0, which possesses the solution *x* = −*c*?/*b*?. This situation is catered for in the following *LinearEquation* schema, where the single root is output along with the message *linear_equation*.

```
┌─LinearEquation──────────────────────────
│ a?, b?, c? : ℝ
│ output! : MESSAGE × seq ℝ
├───────────────────────────────
│ a? = 0
│ b? ≠ 0
│ ∃ x : ℝ ; message : MESSAGE •
│ x = -c?/b?
│ message = linear_equation
│ output! = (message, < x >)
└───────────────────────────────────────
```

If both *a*? and *b*? are zero, the quadratic equation reduces to the very simple equation *c*? = 0. If the input value of *c*? is not zero, the equation becomes inconsistent. The following *InconsistentEquation* schema, to deal with this case, is as follows.

```
┌─InconsistentEquation──────────────────
│ a?, b?, c? : ℝ
│ output! : MESSAGE × seq ℝ
├───────────────────────────
│ a? = 0
│ b? = 0
│ c? ≠ 0
│ ∃ message : MESSAGE •
│ message = inconsistent_equation
│ output! = (message, < >)
└──────────────────────────────────
```

Finally, if all the coefficients of the quadratic are equal to zero, then any value of x will satisfy the equation $a?*x*x + b?*x + c? = 0$. This degenerate case is handled by the following *DegenerateCase* schema which, for simplicity, outputs an empty sequence along with the message *degenerate_case*.

```
┌─DegenerateCase──────────────────
│ a?, b?, c? : ℝ
│ output! : MESSAGE × seq ℝ
├───────────────────────────
│ a? = 0
│ b? = 0
│ c? = 0
│ ∃ message : MESSAGE •
│ message = degenerate_case
│ output! = (message, < >)
└──────────────────────────────────
```

If we regard these last three schemas as exceptions of one kind or another, then we can define a schema called *Exceptions* as follows.

$$Exceptions \triangleq LinearEquation \lor InconsistentEquation \lor DegenerateCase$$

In terms of *Exceptions* and *QuadraticCases* we thus define the required quadratic equation solver schema to be given by

$$Quadsolver \triangleq QuadraticCases \lor Exceptions$$

As a schema it specifies how the software can accept any three real numbers $a?$, $b?$ and $c?$ as input and return, as output, a suitable message together with the appropriate roots, where they exist.

11.3 ELECTRONIC MAIL

This section looks at the specification of an Email system. The specification involves the use of sequences, but also provides the opportunity to introduce schema types into specifications. Schema types were first mentioned in Chapter 3 in the context of type constructors in Z. Both the Email specification considered here, and the specification of the logic puzzle considered next, require the use of schema types.

System requirements
The prime function of the Email system is to enable users of the system to send items of mail from their own workstations to other users in the network. Items of mail, created by users at their workstations, are deposited in their electronic out-trays before being posted. The system checks the format of all mail items to ensure that the sender and recipients have been identified. When users clear their out-tray all items are date stamped, assigned a unique reference number, and are posted by the system to the electronic in-trays of the intended recipients. Users can read the contents of their in-trays and collect any items of mail from them.

System state
The basic types we shall need can be parachuted in as follows.

$[NAME, CHAR]$

From these basic types we can now construct a schema type called *ITEM* as follows.

```
┌─ITEM──────────────────────
│ to : seq NAME
│ from : NAME
│ date : seq CHAR
│ ref : seq CHAR
│ message : seq CHAR
└───────────────────────────
```

A schema type is nothing more than a set of schemas. Here items of mail of schema type *ITEM* are being declared to contain five components, namely a sequence of names called *to*, to whom the item is addressed; the name of the sender, called *from*; a sequence of characters, called *date*, representing the date the item was sent; a unique reference, called *ref*; and the text of the item, called *message*.

In terms of these basic and constructed types, the state of the system can now be specified. The state schema gives a description of the in-trays and out-trays of users of the system, and includes a directory which gives the user's name for each workstation number. The domain of the directory function is the set $\mathbb{N}$, and the assumption is that the system only supports a finite number of user workstations.

```
┌─State──────────────────────────────────────
│ intrays, outtrays : ℕ ⇸ seq ITEM
│ directory : ℕ ⇸ NAME
├────────────────────────────────
│ #dom directory = #ran directory
│ dom directory ⊆ dom intrays
│ dom intrays = dom outtrays
│
│ ∀ n : (dom intrays) \ dom directory •
│ intrays n = < >
│ outtrays n = < >
│
│ ∀ n₁,n₂ : dom directory •
│ ∀ m₁,m₂ : ℕ | m₁ ∈ dom(intrays n₁) ∧
│                m₂ ∈ dom(intrays n₂) •
│ intrays n₁(m₁).ref = intrays n₂(m₂).ref ⇒
│ intrays n₁(m₁) = intrays n₂(m₂)
└────────────────────────────────────────────
```

We see that the in-trays and out-trays of particular workstations are modelled as sequences of mail items. In the predicate we see that every user has a workstation, but that not every workstation in the network has a user. The third line states that every workstation has an in-tray and an out-tray. The middle section of the predicate states that workstations which are not in use should have no items of mail in their in-trays or out-trays. The last section of the predicate states that, if two mail items have the same reference number on them, they must be the same mail item. In this last section of the predicate it is important to note that

$$intrays\ n_1(m_1)\ .\ ref$$

stands for the reference number on the m_1th mail item in the in-tray of the n_1th workstation. The dot notation used here is the standard way of accessing any particular component from an expression that is of schema type. The dot notation is used extensively in what follows.

The initial state schema

An initial state can be specified as follows.

```
┌─InitState──────────────────
│ State
├──────────────────
│ directory = { }
│ ∀ n : dom intrays •
│ intrays n = < >
│ outtrays n = < >
└──────────────────────────
```

There are no users of the system and the in-trays and out-trays of workstations in the system are all empty.

Adding a new user

The operation to add a new user to the system can be specified via the following *Add* schema.

```
┌─Add──────────────────────────
│ ΔState
│ new? : NAME
│ num? : ℕ
├──────────────────────
│ new? ∉ ran directory
│ num? ∈ dom intrays
│ num? ∉ dom directory
│ intrays' = intrays
│ outrays' = outtrays
│ directory' = directory ∪ {num? ↦ new?}
└──────────────────────────────
```

The new user must not already be in the directory and the workstation number must exist and not be in use. The new user is added to the system by adding the maplet $num? \mapsto new?$ to the function *directory*.

Sending an item of mail to the out-tray

Items of mail created by users are sent to their out-trays ready for posting. The operation of sending an item of mail to the out-tray makes use of a binary relation called *formatOK*, that specifies the correct format for mail items. The definition of the *formatOK* relation is as follows.

$$
\begin{array}{l}
formatOK : NAME \leftrightarrow ITEM \\
\hline
\forall\ name : NAME ;\ item : ITEM \bullet \\
(name, item) \in formatOK \Leftrightarrow \\
item.to \neq \langle\ \rangle \\
item.from = name \\
item.date = \langle\ \rangle \\
item.ref = \langle\ \rangle \\
item.message \neq \langle\ \rangle
\end{array}
$$

Items should not contain a date or a reference number as these will be supplied by the system when the mail is posted. The assumption is that an item of mail is sent to someone, and that the message is never empty.

The operation called *UserToOut* enables an item of mail, created at a workstation by a user, to be checked and deposited in their out-tray ready for sending when the user invokes the appropriate posting operation. The *UserToOut* schema, which makes use of the *formatOK* relation, can be written as follows.

$$
\begin{array}{l}
\textit{UserToOut} \\
\hline
\Delta State \\
number? : \mathbb{N} \\
item? : ITEM \\
\hline
number? \in \mathrm{dom}\ directory \\
(directory(number?), item?) \in formatOK \\
directory(number?) \notin \mathrm{ran}(item.to) \\
\mathrm{ran}(item.to) \subseteq \mathrm{ran}(directory) \\
intrays' = intrays \\
outtrays' = outtrays \oplus \{number? \mapsto \\
\qquad\qquad outtrays(number?) \frown \langle item \rangle\} \\
directory' = directory
\end{array}
$$

The preconditions for this operation to work are that the workstation number of the user must be in the domain of the directory function; the item to be posted must be in the correct format; the item must not be self addressed; and the recipients of the item should belong to the range of the directory function. When these are all satisfied the system state is updated by concatenating the new item to the sequence of items already in the user's in-tray.

Collecting an item of mail from the in-tray

The following schema, called *CollectFromIn*, specifies how users can remove an item of mail, selected by its reference number, from their in–tray.

```
┌─CollectFromIn──────────────────────────────
│ ΔState
│ number? : ℕ
│ r? : seq CHAR
│ item! : ITEM
├──────────────────────────────
│ number? ∈ dom directory
│ ∃ item : ran(intrays(number?)) •
│ item.ref = r?
│ item! = item
│ intrays' = intrays ⊕ {number? ↦
│            squash(intrays(number?) ⩥ {item})}
│ outtrays' = outtrays
│ directory' = directory
└──────────────────────────────────────────
```

An item that is removed from the in–tray is created as output to be read by the user. The user must supply the reference number *r*? of the item to be removed.

Posting items to in–trays

The operation whereby items of mail are posted, via the system, to the in–trays of other users requires a utility function called *stamped*, which we shall now define. When items in a user's in–tray are posted they are date stamped, and a unique reference number is put on the item. The *stamped* function is designed to do this; it uses two other utility functions

$$datenew : \text{seq } CHAR \nrightarrow \text{seq } CHAR$$

$$newref : \text{seq } CHAR \nrightarrow \text{seq } CHAR$$

which furnish the current date and a new (and unique) reference number respectively. The sequence of characters, which each function requires for this purpose, is supplied by the system. The definition of the *stamped* function is as follows.

$$
\begin{array}{|l}
stamped : ITEM \nrightarrow ITEM \\
\hline
\forall\ item_1, item_2 : ITEM \mid (item_1.from, item_1) \\
\qquad\qquad\qquad\qquad\qquad\qquad \in formatOK \bullet \\
item_2 = stamped(item_1) \Rightarrow \\
item_2.to = item_1.to \\
item_2.from = item_1.from \\
\exists\ c_1, c_2 : \text{seq } CHAR \bullet \\
item_2.date = datenew\ c_1 \\
item_2.ref = newref\ c_2 \\
item_2.message = item_1.message
\end{array}
$$

The stamped function, therefore, only adds a date and a reference; other aspects of the item remain the same.

When the items are posted they are sent to the in–trays of people whose names are contained in the sequence of names in the *to* component of the items. The *PostToIn* operation posts stamped items to the in–trays of these people; the schema which specifies the operation is as follows.

$$
\begin{array}{|l}
\textit{PostToIn} \\
\hline
\Delta State \\
number? : \mathbb{N} \\
\hline
number? \in \text{dom } directory \\
outtrays\ number? \neq \langle\ \rangle \\
outtrays' = outtrays \oplus \{number? \mapsto \langle\ \rangle\} \\
intrays' = intrays \oplus \{n : \mathbb{N} ; list : \text{seq } ITEM \mid \\
n \in (\text{dom } directory) \setminus \{number?\} \land \\
list = squash(outtrays(number?) \rhd \{item' : ITEM \mid \\
\exists\ item : ITEM \bullet item' = stamped(item) \land \\
directory(n) \in \text{ran}(item\ .to)\}) \bullet \\
n \mapsto intrays(n) \frown list\} \\
\hline
\end{array}
$$

When the items are posted the out–tray of the poster is emptied and the in–trays of others are updated accordingly.

Removing a user from the Email system

The last operation we shall specify, that changes the state of our system, is the operation that specifies how a user of the system is removed. We specify such a remove operation via a schema called *RemoveUser* as follows.

$$
\begin{array}{|l}
\hline
\textit{RemoveUser} \\
\Delta State \\
number? : \mathbb{N} \\
\hline
number? \in \mathrm{dom}\ directory \\
intrays\ number? = \langle\ \rangle \\
outtrays\ number? = \langle\ \rangle \\
intrays' = intrays \\
outtrays' = outtrays \\
directory' = directory \setminus \\
\qquad\qquad \{number? \mapsto directory\ number?\} \\
\hline
\end{array}
$$

Here we are insisting that users have emptied their in-trays and posted their out-tray contents before being removed.

System operations that query the state

The only operation we shall specify that simply queries the system is the operation that enables a user to create an item of mail, that happens to be in the in-tray, for the purposes of reading it. Although the item of mail is created, the original copy is still left in the in-tray, thus leaving the system state unchanged.

The operation of reading an item of mail in the in-tray is specified by the following *ReadFromIn* schema.

$$
\begin{array}{|l}
\hline
\textit{ReadFromIn} \\
\Xi State \\
number? : \mathbb{N} \\
r? : \mathrm{seq}\ CHAR \\
item! : ITEM \\
\hline
number? \in \mathrm{dom}\ directory \\
\exists\ item : \mathrm{ran}\ intrays(number?) \bullet \\
item\ .ref = r? \\
item! = item \\
\hline
\end{array}
$$

The item with reference number *r?* is created and set equal to *item!*, but remains in the in-tray.

Creating the robust interface

Although we do not build the robust user interfaces explicitly, we list the error reports that are needed for each schema we have written. These error reports help us to see what error schemas to create to specify the complete system. The reports that are required for each error schema can be written down by inspecting the preconditions involved. For each of the operations that we have specified, the error reports can be written out as follows.

Add :- *already_user*, *number_in_use*, *no_such_number*

UserToOut :- *no_such_number*, *wrong_format*, *self_addressed*, *recipient_not_known*

CollectFromIn :- *no_such_number*, *ref_not_known*

PostToIn :- *no_such_number*, *no_mail_to_post*

RemoveUser :- *no_such_number*, *intray_not_empty*, *outtray_not_empty*

ReadFromIn :- *no_such_number*, *ref_not_known*

From here on the production of the complete system is fairly mechanical, and is left to the reader to complete as an exercise.

11.4 SPECIFYING THE SOLUTION TO A LOGIC PUZZLE

In our final example we consider a non-trivial logic puzzle, and the task of specifying its solution. The particular logic puzzle is one that has appeared in several computing journals and in books on logic programming.

- There are five houses, each of a different colour and inhabited by a man of a different nationality, with a different pet, drink, and brand of cigarette.

  1. The Englishman lives in the red house.
  2. The Spaniard owns the dog.
  3. Coffee is drunk in the green house.
  4. The Ukranian drinks tea.
  5. The green house is immediately to the right of the ivory house.
  6. The Winston smoker owns snails.
  7. Kools are smoked in the yellow house.
  8. Milk is drunk in the middle house.
  9. The Norwegian lives in the first house on the left.

10. The man who smokes Chesterfields lives in the house next to the man with the fox.

11. Kools are smoked in the house next to the house where the horse is kept.

12. The Lucky Strike smoker drinks orange juice.

13. The Japanese smokes Parliaments.

14. The Norwegian lives next to the blue house.

Who owns the zebra and who drinks water?

Clearly this is a non-trivial problem. The way we approach the problem of specifying the solution is firstly to capture the essential features of the five houses involved, and then develop our knowledge of the state by systematically adding in the information that each clue provides. Having built up a specification of the state, we then write a schema to enable us to query this description in order to extract the information needed to tell us who owns the zebra and who drinks water.

We begin by parachuting in the following basic types.

$[COLOUR, NATIONALITY, PET, DRINK, CIGARETTE]$

In terms of these we construct a schema type called *HOUSE* as follows.

```
┌─HOUSE──────────────────
│ col : COLOUR
│ nat : NATIONALITY
│ pet : PET
│ dr : DRINK
│ cig : CIGARETTE
└────────────────────────
```

Since we know that there are five houses, each of a different colour, inhabited by a man of a different nationality, with a different pet, drink and brand of cigarette, we start by capturing this information in the *FiveHouses* schema given below.

```
┌─FiveHouses──────────────────────────────
│ a, b, c, d, e : HOUSE
│ houses : seq HOUSE
├─────────────────────────────
│ houses = <a,b,c,d,e>
│ #ran(houses) = 5
│ ∀ h₁,h₂ : ran houses •
│ h₁.col = h₂.col ⇒ h₁ = h₂
│ h₁.nat = h₂.nat ⇒ h₁ = h₂
│ h₁.pet = h₂.pet ⇒ h₁ = h₂
│ h₁.dr = h₂.dr ⇒ h₁ = h₂
│ h₁.cig = h₂.cig ⇒ h₁ = h₂
└──────────────────────────────────────
```

From this schema it is clear that we have chosen to call the five houses involved a, b, c, d and e. We have assumed that they exist in a row called *houses*, and the specific order we have chosen is given by the sequence $<a, b, c, d, e>$, where a will be furthest to the left and e furthest to the right in the row. The predicate in the schema specifies that the colours, nationalities, pets, drinks and brand of cigarette in the five houses are all different, as required.

To begin the process of adding in the information provided by the clues, we need to define what is meant by a house being to the right or next to another. This is easily done by modelling each property as a binary relation as follows.

```
│ next_to : (HOUSE × HOUSE) ↔ seq HOUSE
│ right_of : (HOUSE × HOUSE) ↔ seq HOUSE
├──────────────────────────────────────
│ ∀ h₁,h₂ : HOUSE ; row : seq HOUSE •
│ ((h₁,h₂),row) ∈ next_to ⇔
│ ∃ s,t : seq HOUSE •
│ s ⁀ <h₁,h₂> ⁀ t = row ∨
│                 s ⁀ <h₂,h₁> ⁀ t = row ∧
│ ((h₁,h₂),row) ∈ right_of ⇔
│ ∃ s,t : seq HOUSE •
│ s ⁀ <h₂,h₁> ⁀ t = row
```

We can now write the 14 schemas that represent the given clues. Each is set out below, without any explanation. The meaning of the declarations and predicates is straightforward.

```
┌─Clue1──────────────────────────
│ FiveHouses
├─────────────────────
│ ∃ x : ran houses •
│ x.nat = english ∧ x.col = red
└────────────────────────────────
```

```
┌─Clue2──────────────────────────
│ FiveHouses
├─────────────────────
│ ∃ x : ran houses •
│ x.nat = spaniard ∧ x.pet = dog
└────────────────────────────────
```

```
┌─Clue3──────────────────────────
│ FiveHouses
├─────────────────────
│ ∃ x : ran houses •
│ x.dr = coffee ∧ x.col = green
└────────────────────────────────
```

```
┌─Clue4──────────────────────────
│ FiveHouses
├─────────────────────
│ ∃ x : ran houses •
│ x.nat = ukranian ∧ x.dr = tea
└────────────────────────────────
```

```
┌─Clue5──────────────────────────
│ FiveHouses
├─────────────────────
│ ∃ x,y : ran houses •
│ x.col = green ∧ y.col = ivory ∧
│ ((x,y), houses) ∈ right_of
└────────────────────────────────
```

```
┌─Clue6──────────────────────────
│ FiveHouses
├─────────────────────
│ ∃ x : ran houses •
│ x.cig = winston ∧ x.pet = snails
└────────────────────────────────
```

```
┌─Clue7──────────────────────────────
│ FiveHouses
├────────────────────────
│ ∃ x : ran houses •
│ x.cig = kools ∧ x.col = yellow
└────────────────────────────────────
```

```
┌─Clue8──────────────────────────────
│ FiveHouses
├────────────────────────
│ c.dr = milk
└────────────────────────────────────
```

```
┌─Clue9──────────────────────────────
│ FiveHouses
├────────────────────────
│ a.nat = norwegian
└────────────────────────────────────
```

```
┌─Clue10─────────────────────────────
│ FiveHouses
├────────────────────────
│ ∃ x,y : ran houses •
│ x.cig = chesterfields ∧ y.pet = fox ∧
│ ((x,y), houses) ∈ next_to
└────────────────────────────────────
```

```
┌─Clue11─────────────────────────────
│ FiveHouses
├────────────────────────
│ ∃ x,y : ran houses •
│ x.cig = kools ∧ y.pet = horse ∧
│ ((x,y), houses) ∈ next_to
└────────────────────────────────────
```

```
┌─Clue12─────────────────────────────
│ FiveHouses
├────────────────────────
│ ∃ x : ran houses •
│ x.cig = lucky_strikes ∧
│ x.dr = orange_juice
└────────────────────────────────────
```

Clue13

$$FiveHouses$$

$$\exists x : \mathrm{ran}\ houses \bullet x.cig = parliaments \land x.nat = japanese$$

Clue14

$$FiveHouses$$

$$\exists x,y : \mathrm{ran}\ houses \bullet x.nat = norwegian \land y.col = blue \land ((x,y), houses) \in next\_to$$

The state of the system is thus the sum total of all the information contained in these 14 clues. We can, therefore, define a schema to specify the state of our five houses as follows.

$$State \mathrel{\widehat{=}} Clue1 \land Clue2 \land Clue3 \land Clue4 \land Clue5 \land Clue6 \land Clue7 \land Clue8 \land Clue9 \land Clue10 \land Clue11 \land Clue12 \land Clue13 \land Clue14$$

To specify the solution to the puzzle, all that remains to do is to define an operation to query this state and output the owner of the zebra and the nationality of the person who drinks water. The following *Solution* schema does this for us.

Solution

$$\Xi State$$
$$x!, y! : NATIONALITY$$

$$\exists p,q : \mathrm{ran}\ houses \bullet p.pet = zebra \land p.nat = x! \land q.dr = water \land q.nat = y!$$

Readers interested in working out the solution may like to know that the Japanese owns the zebra and the Norwegian drinks water.

CHAPTER 12

Concluding remarks

12.1 INTRODUCTION

In this concluding chapter we reflect briefly on the aims of the book and on the presentation of the content. We look at the skills and knowledge that the book was designed to impart, and consider where the interested reader might go from here to develop their knowledge further.

The book has been written over a period of three years. During this time there have been significant developments in both industry and academia on the formal methods front. We look at these developments, and then give a short assessment of the progress being made in industrialising formal methods.

12.2 REFLECTING ON THE AIMS AND PRESENTATION

Our aim, from the outset, has been to provide a thorough insight into the advantages to be gained from using mathematics in the software development process, and to provide readers with the motivation and means to become more effective programmers. We hope we have succeeded in achieving this aim, and that readers are now sufficiently confident to begin to use formal methods, for real, in designing and building software. One major problem surrounding formal methods is the perception that the underpinning mathematics is difficult. Again, we hope we have enlightened readers significantly in this respect, and allayed many of the fears that exist, particularly amongst programmers, regarding the subject of mathematics.

As far as learning formal methods is concerned, our strategy has been clear. Firstly, we have placed great store on motivating the mathematics by showing its use in practical problems. Experience over many years of teaching students, whose main subject is perceived not to be mathematics, has shown that they learn best when the immediate relevance of what is being taught is clearly illustrated. Learning via motivating examples and seeing mathematics in action, as soon as is practicable, are key ingredients to successful mathematics applications teaching. For this reason we chose not to cover all the mathematics first, before moving on to look at examples. We developed the mathematics of software construction in a progressive way, mixing mathematics with specification, so that the former could be learned firmly within the context of software engineering.

Secondly, we have kept the book at an introductory level and have not attempted a comprehensive study of the mathematics of software construction, or of the Z language. What we have provided is a basic toolkit that enables readers to specify many software systems and reason formally about them. Our experience has been that a little mathematics, well understood, goes a long way when developing formal specifications, and that an introductory text is preferable to attempting a more ambitious coverage when the base of mathematics preknowledge is O-level or GCSE.

Thirdly, our experience of teaching discrete mathematics has taught us of the need for a standard notation within which to present the mathematics. Academics are notorious for inventing and using their own notation and symbols, which very often leads to confusion. The conscious decision to standardise on the Z notation was taken for this very reason. The formal methods community at large has a great number of zealots and purists who are bound to ask why the Z notation was chosen in preference to other standard notations. Our feeling is that Z is an excellent notation to work with, and one with which a growing number of programmers are now familiar. Certainly an understanding of Z, such as this book provides, should enable interested readers quickly to come to grips with other specification languages.

With regard to the skills and knowledge that this book was designed to impart, the following points are relevant. The book was conceived to be an introductory text, capable of being read and understood by interested programmers possessing little mathematical knowledge. There are thus many topics in discrete mathematics that are not covered, such as graph theory, partial orders, and category theory. What is covered, however, is the basis on which these more advanced topics are built, and readers should therefore be well placed to learn about these topics from the knowledge they now possess.

Regarding Z, it is important to realise that there is much of the notation still to be covered. Free types, generic definitions, bags and other kinds of functions, for example, have not been covered in any detail. Also, refinement from Z to code is far more developed in the literature than is evident from the brief coverage given. Interested readers are thus urged to study the more advanced texts on Z, mentioned in the Bibliography, such as those written by Diller, Spivey or Woodcock & Loomes. Alternatively there are many training courses on specification and refinement for those who wish to become experts in the use of the Z language.

This book, then, should be regarded as a springboard to acquiring further knowledge in both discrete mathematics and in specification languages generally. A working knowledge of Z will certainly help when it comes to learning about other standard specification languages.

12.3 ASSESSING WHERE FORMAL METHODS ARE LEADING

In Chapter 1 we stated that the discipline of software engineering was at a turning point with regard to the use of formal methods. This is still largely true.

Academia is convinced of the need for formal methods, and most computer-related courses at degree and masters level now include modules on formal methods. Industry, however, is still loath to embrace wholeheartedly this new way of developing software. In the main, technical management remains to be convinced that the rather high early costs associated with the use of formal methods are justified by the gains later in the software life cycle. Managers are also concerned about the effects that wholesale changes in working practices implied by formal methods might bring, and at the cost of retraining a largely non-mathematical workforce in order to exploit formal methods. Staff, too, are concerned about the need to cope with mathematics in a discipline area that initially was thought not to require mathematics. So, despite the high expectations for formal methods in the early eighties, their uptake by industry has generally been less than had been hoped for.

There have been encouraging developments that are gradually shifting the balance in favour of a wider acceptance of formal methods by industry. In areas where safety-critical and secure systems are being developed the use of formal methods is on the increase, driven by customer requirements that the software be developed using rigorous and verifiable methods. More generally, there is growing evidence that the wider use of formal methods can lead to significant increases in productivity and enhanced quality. IBM's recent experience using Z to specify their Customer Information Control System (CICS), and the development of the Inmos T800 Transputer, also using Z, have helped to convince management that high early costs can, indeed, reap genuine benefits.

In the skills update and CASE tools area, some of the barriers to industrialising formal methods are being removed gradually. Teaching material, designed to give a gentle and sympathetic introduction to formal methods, now exists and is in a form suitable for the many programmers who require it. CASE tools are at last becoming available to help the developer create specifications and to verify implementations; tools to assist in specification animation, in order to validate specifications against user requirements, are also being developed. Thus many of the problem areas, often cited by industry as reasons for not taking formal methods seriously, are now being addressed.

In the Z area, the UK Z User Group is active and there are clear signs that the infrastructure needed to support a thriving community of Z users, in both industry and academia, will soon be in place. If the current DTI-funded ZIP project is successful, for example, then we should shortly have a BSI standard Z notation, a methods handbook, and a suite of support tools for Z.

So the outlook for the nineties is encouraging, and at long last the much awaited uptake of formal methods by industry seems set to occur. Let us hope that it does.

Answers to exercises

CHAPTER 2

1. (a) (i) $\{jill, sue\}$
   (ii) $\{jack, jill, den, sue, bill, andy, kylie\}$
   (iii) $\{jill, andy\}$
   (iv) $\{jill, sue, andy\}$
   (v) $\{jack, den, sue, bill, kylie\}$
   (vi) $\{jill, jack, den\}$

   (b) (i) $\{ \{ \}, \{jack\}, \{jill\}, \{den\}, \{andy\}, \{jack, jill\}, \{jack, den\}, \{jack, andy\}, \{jill, den\}, \{jill, andy\}, \{den, andy\}, \{jack, jill, den\}, \{jack, den, andy\}, \{jack, jill, andy\}, \{jill, den, andy\}, \{jack, jill, den, andy\} \}$
   (ii) 20
   (iii) 16

3. (i) T (ii) T (iii) F

4. When $A = B$

CHAPTER 3

1.

```
┌─Remove──────────────────────
│ ΔState
│ staff? : STAFF_ID
├─────────────────
│ staff? ∈ out
│ in' = in
│ out' = out \ {staff?}
│ users' = users \ {staff?}
└─────────────────────────────
```

2. $RCheckOut \mathrel{\widehat=} (CheckOut \wedge Success) \vee CheckOutError$

   $CheckOutError \mathrel{\widehat=} StaffOut \vee NotUser$

```
┌─StaffOut────────────────────
│ ΞState
│ staff? : STAFF_ID
│ message! : REPORT
├─────────────────
│ staff? ∈ out
│ message! = already_out
└─────────────────────────────
```

$RRemove \mathrel{\widehat=} (Remove \land Success) \lor RemoveError$

$RemoveError \mathrel{\widehat=} StillIn \lor NotUser$

```
┌─StillIn──────────────────────────
│ ΞState
│ staff? : STAFF_ID
│ message! : REPORT
├──────────────────────
│ staff? ∈ in
│ message! = still_in
└──────────────────────────────────
```

3. (a) $RQueryForIn \mathrel{\widehat=} QueryForIn \land Success$

```
┌─QueryForIn───────────────────────
│ ΞState
│ in! : ℙ STAFF_ID
├──────────────────────
│ in! = in
└──────────────────────────────────
```

(b) $RQueryForOut \mathrel{\widehat=} QueryForOut \land Success$

```
┌─QueryForOut──────────────────────
│ ΞState
│ out! : ℙ STAFF_ID
├──────────────────────
│ out! = out
└──────────────────────────────────
```

(c) $RQueryForUsers \mathrel{\widehat=} QueryForUsers \land Success$

```
┌─QueryForUsers────────────────────
│ ΞState
│ users! : ℙ STAFF_ID
├──────────────────────
│ users! = users
└──────────────────────────────────
```

CHAPTER 4

1. $RAdd \mathrel{\widehat=} (Add \land Success) \lor AddError$

$AddError \mathrel{\widehat=} Full \lor NameIn$

```
┌─Full──────────────────────────
│ ΞDirectory
│ message! : REPORT
├───────────────────
│ #dir = 100
│ message = directory_full
└───────────────────────────────
```

```
┌─NameIn────────────────────────
│ ΞDirectory
│ name? : NAME
│ message! : REPORT
├───────────────────
│ #dir < 100
│ name? ∈ dom dir
│ message! = name_in_directory
└───────────────────────────────
```

RRemove ≙ (*Remove* ∧ *Success*) ∨ *RemoveError*

RemoveError ≙ *NameNotIn*

```
┌─NameNotIn─────────────────────
│ ΞDirectory
│ name? : NAME
│ message! : REPORT
├───────────────────
│ name? ∉ dom dir
│ message! = name_not_known
└───────────────────────────────
```

RQueryForNumber ≙ (*QueryForNumber* ∧ *Success*) ∨
QueryForNumberError

QueryForNumberError ≙ *NameNotIn*

3.

```
│ power : (ℝ × ℕ) ⟶ ℝ
├───────────────────
│ ∀ x : ℝ ; n : ℕ •
│ x = 0 ⇒ power(x,n) = 0
│ x ≠ 0 ∧ n = 0 ⇒ power(x,n) = 1
│ x ≠ 0 ∧ n ≠ 0 ⇒ power(x,n) = x*power(x,n-1)
```

4.

```
┌─Account────────────────────────────
│ balance, od_limit : ACC_NO ⇸ ℤ
├──────────────────────────
│ dom balance = dom od_limit
│ ∀ x : dom balance •
│ balance(x) ≥ -od_limit(x)
│ od_limit(x) ≥ 0
└────────────────────────────────────
```

CHAPTER 5

1. $REPORT ::= ok \mid current\_user \mid negative\_odl \mid not\_known \mid invalid\_deposit \mid invalid\_withdrawal \mid insufficient\_funds \mid non\_zero\_balance \mid invalid\_odl$

$ROpen \mathrel{\widehat{=}} (Open \land Success) \lor OpenError$

$OpenError \mathrel{\widehat{=}} CurrentUser \lor NegOdl$

```
┌─Success────────────────────────────
│ message! = REPORT
├──────────────────────────
│ message! = ok
└────────────────────────────────────
```

```
┌─CurrentUser────────────────────────
│ ΞAccount
│ new? : ACC_NO
│ message! : REPORT
├──────────────────────────
│ new? ∈ dom balance
│ message! = current_user
└────────────────────────────────────
```

```
┌─NegOdl─────────────────────────────
│ ΞAccount
│ new? : ACC_NO
│ odl? : ℤ
│ message! : REPORT
├──────────────────────────
│ new? ∉ dom balance
│ odl? < 0
│ message! = negative_odl
└────────────────────────────────────
```

$RDeposit \mathrel{\widehat{=}} (Deposit \land Success) \lor DepositError$

$DepositError \mathrel{\widehat{=}} InvalidAccount \lor InvalidDeposit$

```
┌─InvalidAccount──────────────
│ ΞAccount
│ user_no? : ACC_NO
│ message! : REPORT
├──────────────────────
│ user_no? ∉ dom balance
│ message! = not_known
└──────────────────────────
```

```
┌─InvalidDeposit──────────────
│ ΞAccount
│ user_no? : ACC_NO
│ amount? : ℤ
│ message! : REPORT
├──────────────────────
│ user_no? ∈ dom balance
│ amount? ≤ 0
│ message! = invalid_deposit
└──────────────────────────
```

$RWithdraw \mathrel{\widehat{=}} (Withdraw \land Success) \lor WithdrawError$

$WithdrawError \mathrel{\widehat{=}} InvalidAccount \lor InvalidWithdrawal$
$\qquad \lor InsufficientFunds$

```
┌─InvalidWithdrawal──────────────
│ ΞAccount
│ user_no? : ACC_NO
│ amount? : ℤ
│ message! : REPORT
├──────────────────────
│ user_no? ∈ dom balance
│ amount? ≤ 0
│ message! = invalid_withdrawal
└──────────────────────────
```

```
┌─InsufficientFunds──────────────
│ ΞAccount
│ user_no? : ACC_NO
│ amount? : ℤ
│ message! : REPORT
├──────────────────────
│ user_no? ∈ dom balance
│ amount? > 0
│ balance(user_no?) - amount < od_limit(user_no?)
│ message! = insufficient_funds
└──────────────────────────
```

RClose ≙ (*Close* ∧ *Success*) ∨ *CloseError*

CloseError ≙ *InvalidAccount* ∨ *NonZeroBalance*

```
┌─NonZeroBalance──────────────────
│ ΞAccount
│ user_no? : ACC_NO
│ message! : REPORT
├─────────────────────────
│ user_no? ∈ dom balance
│ balance user_no? ≠ 0
│ message! = non_zero_balance
└─────────────────────────────
```

RQueryForAccounts ≙ *QueryForAccounts* ∧ *Success*

2. *RChangeOdl* ≙ (*ChangeOdl* ∧ *Success*) ∨ *ChangeOdlError*

ChangeOdlError ≙ *InvalidAccount* ∨ *NegativeOdl* ∨ *InvalidOdl*

```
┌─ChangeOdl───────────────────────
│ ΔAccount
│ user_no? : ACC_NO
│ odl? : ℤ
├─────────────────────────
│ user_no? ∈ dom balance
│ odl? ≥ 0
│ balance(user_no?) ≥ -odl?
│ balance' = balance
│ od_limit' = od_limit ⊕ {user_no? ↦ -odl?}
└─────────────────────────────
```

```
┌─NegativeOdl─────────────────────
│ ΞAccount
│ user_no? : ACC_NO
│ odl? : ℤ
│ message! : REPORT
├─────────────────────────
│ user_no? ∈ dom balance
│ odl? < 0
│ message! = negative_odl
└─────────────────────────────
```

$$
\begin{array}{l}
\textit{InvalidOdl} \\
\hline
\Xi Account \\
user\_no? : ACC\_NO \\
odl? : \mathbb{Z} \\
message! : REPORT \\
\hline
user\_no? \in \mathrm{dom}\ balance \\
odl? > 0 \\
balance\ user\_no? < -odl? \\
message! = invalid\_odl \\
\hline
\end{array}
$$

3.

$$
\begin{array}{l}
\textit{QueryForStudents} \\
\hline
\Xi Account \\
studbalances! : \mathbb{P}\ \mathbb{Z} \\
studod\_limits! : \mathbb{P}\ \mathbb{Z} \\
\hline
studbalances! = \mathrm{ran}(StudentNumbers \lhd balance) \\
studod\_limits! = \mathrm{ran}(StudentNumbers \lhd od\_limit) \\
\hline
\end{array}
$$

CHAPTER 7

1.

$$
\begin{array}{l}
insert : (X \times \mathbb{N}_1 \times \mathrm{seq}\ X) \rightarrowtail\!\!\!\!\!+ \ \mathrm{seq}\ X \\
\hline
\forall\ x : X ;\ n : \mathbb{N}_1 ;\ s : \mathrm{seq}\ X \mid n \leq \#s + 1 \bullet \\
insert(x,n,s) = (1..n-1 \lhd s) \frown \langle x \rangle \frown \\
\qquad\qquad squash(n..\#s \lhd s)
\end{array}
$$

2.

$$
\begin{array}{l}
cut : (\mathbb{N}_1 \times \mathrm{seq}\ X) \rightarrowtail\!\!\!\!\!+ \ (\mathrm{seq}\ X \times \mathrm{seq}\ X) \\
\hline
\forall\ n : \mathbb{N}_1 ;\ s : \mathrm{seq}\ X \mid n \leq \#s \bullet \\
cut(n,s) = ((1..n-1 \lhd s),\ squash(n..\#s \lhd s))
\end{array}
$$

3.

$$
\begin{array}{l}
sum : \mathrm{seq}\ \mathbb{N} \longrightarrow \mathbb{N} \\
\hline
sum(\langle\ \rangle) = 0 \\
\forall\ s : \mathrm{seq}\ \mathbb{N} \mid s \neq \langle\ \rangle \bullet \\
sum(s) = s(1) + sum(tail(s))
\end{array}
$$

4. (i)

```
┌─InitScoreSheet──────────────────────────
│ ScoreSheet
├──────────────────────
│ scores : {first ↦ < >, second ↦ < >}
│ requires : {first ↦ 501, second ↦ 501}
└─────────────────────────────────────────
```

(ii)

```
┌─AddScore────────────────────────────────
│ ΔScoreSheet
│ player? : PLAYER
│ score? : ℕ
├──────────────────────
│ player? ∈ dom scores
│ score? ≤ 180
│ requires player? > score?
│ scores' = scores ⊕ {player? ↦
│           scores(player?) ⁀ <score?>}
│ requires' = requires ⊕ {player? ↦
│           requires(player?) - score?}
└─────────────────────────────────────────
```

(iii)

```
┌─WinningScore────────────────────────────
│ ΔScoreSheet
│ player? : PLAYER
│ score? : ℕ
├──────────────────────
│ player? ∈ dom scores
│ score? ≤ 180
│ requires player? = score?
│ scores' = scores ⊕ {player? ↦
│           scores(player?) ⁀ <score?>}
│ requires' = requires ⊕ {player? ↦ 0}
└─────────────────────────────────────────
```

CHAPTER 8

1.

```
┌─Withdraw────────────────────────
│ ΔLibrary
│ ΞBorrowers
│ copy? : COPY
├──────────────────────
│ copy? ∈ copies_in
│ copies_in' = copies_in \ {copy?}
│ copies_out' = copies_out
│ copies' = copies ⩥ {copy?}
└─────────────────────────────────
```

2.

```
┌─QueryForAvailability──────────
│ ΞLibrary
│ available! : ℙ BOOK
├───────────────────────
│ available! = dom(copies ▷ copies_in)
└───────────────────────────────
```

3.

$$REPORT ::= ok \mid already\_user \mid already\_copy \mid unknown\_user \mid not\_in\_library \mid out\_on\_loan$$

$$RJoin \mathrel{\widehat{=}} (Join \land Success) \lor JoinError$$

$$JoinError \mathrel{\widehat{=}} AlreadyUser$$

```
┌─Success───────────────────────
│ message! : REPORT
├───────────────────────
│ message! = ok
└───────────────────────────────
```

```
┌─AlreadyUser───────────────────
│ ΞLibrary
│ new_user? : PERSON
│ message! : REPORT
├───────────────────────
│ new_user ∈ users
│ message! = already_user
└───────────────────────────────
```

$$RAddCopy \mathrel{\widehat{=}} (AddCopy \land Success) \lor AddCopyError$$

$$AddCopyError \mathrel{\widehat{=}} AlreadyCopy$$

```
┌─AlreadyCopy─────────────────────────
│ ΞLibrary
│ copy? : COPY
│ book? : BOOK
│ message! : REPORT
├───────────────────────
│ (book? ↦ copy?) ∈ copies
│ message! = already_copy
└───────────────────────────────
```

$$RIssueCopy \mathrel{\widehat{=}} (IssueCopy \land Success) \lor IssueCopyError$$

$$IssueCopy\ Error \mathrel{\widehat{=}} UnknownUser \lor CopyOut \lor NotInLibrary$$

UnknownUser

$\Xi Library$
$user? : PERSON$
$message! : REPORT$

$user? \notin users$
$message! = unknown\_user$

CopyOut

$\Xi Library$
$user? : PERSON$
$copy? : COPY$
$message! : REPORT$

$user? \in users$
$copy \in copies\_out$
$message! = out\_on\_loan$

NotInLibrary

$\Xi Library$
$user? : PERSON$
$copy? : COPY$
$message! : REPORT$

$user? \in users$
$copy \notin \mathrm{ran}\ copies$
$message! = not\_in\_library$

$RWithdraw \mathrel{\widehat{=}} (Withdraw \land Success) \lor WithdrawError$

$WithdrawError \mathrel{\widehat{=}} Out \lor NotIn$

Out

$\Xi Library$
$copy? : COPY$
$message! : REPORT$

$copy? \in copies\_out$
$message! = out\_on\_loan$

```
┌─NotIn──────────────────────────────────
│ ΞLibrary
│ copy? : COPY
│ message! : REPORT
├──────────────────────────
│ copy? ∉ ran copies
│ message! = not_in_library
└────────────────────────────────────────
```

$RQueryForBooks \mathrel{\widehat=} (QueryForBooks \land Success) \lor$
$\quad QueryForBooksError$

$QueryForBooksError \mathrel{\widehat=} UnknownUser$

$RQueryForAvailability \mathrel{\widehat=} QueryForAvailability \land Success$

Bibliography

The following books are recommended as further reading for those interested in extending their knowledge of both discrete mathematics and the Z specification language.

Diller A. (1990). *Z: An introduction to formal methods.* John Wiley & Sons, Chichester

Hayes I (ed) (1987). *Specification case studies.* Prentice Hall, Hemel Hempstead

Ince DC. (1988). *An introduction to discrete mathematics and formal system specification.* Oxford University Press, Oxford

Potter B, Sinclair J & Till D. (1991). *An introduction to formal specification and Z.* Prentice Hall, Hemel Hempstead

Slater GL (ed) (1987). *Essential mathematics for software engineers.* Peter Peregrinus, London

Spivey JM. (1989). *The Z notation: A reference manual.* Prentice Hall, Hemel Hempstead

Woodcock JCP & Loomes M. (1988). *Software engineering mathematics: Formal methods demystified.* Pitman, London

Index of symbols

Index

In this Index, the main treatments of topics are indicated by bold page numbers.

Mathematics and its Applications

Series Editor: G. M. BELL,

Professor of Mathematics, King's College London, University of London

Author	Title
Blum, W.	**Applications and Modelling in Learning and Teaching Mathematics**
Brown, R.	**Topology: A Geometric Account of General Topology, Homotopy Types and the Fundamental Groupoid**
Burghes, D.N. & Borrie, M.	**Modelling with Differential Equations**
Burghes, D.N. & Downs, A.M.	**Modern Introduction to Classical Mechanics and Control**
Burghes, D.N. & Graham, A.	**Introduction to Control Theory, including Optimal Control**
Burghes, D.N., Huntley, I. & McDonald, J.	**Applying Mathematics**
Burghes, D.N. & Wood, A.D.	**Mathematical Models in the Social, Management and Life Sciences**
Butkovskiy, A.G.	**Green's Functions and Transfer Functions Handbook**
Cartwright, M.	**Fourier Methods: for Mathematicians, Scientists and Engineers**
Cerny, I.	**Complex Domain Analysis**
Chorlton, F.	**Textbook of Dynamics, 2nd Edition**
Chorlton, F.	**Vector and Tensor Methods**
Cohen, D.E.	**Computability and Logic**
Cordier, J.-M. & Porter, T.	**Shape Theory: Categorical Methods of Approximation**
Crapper, G.D.	**Introduction to Water Waves**
Cross, M. & Moscardini, A.O.	**Learning the Art of Mathematical Modelling**
Cullen, M.R.	**Linear Models in Biology**
Dunning-Davies, J.	**Mathematical Methods for Mathematicians, Physical Scientists and Engineers**
Eason, G., Coles, C.W. & Gettinby, G.	**Mathematics and Statistics for the Biosciences**
El Jai, A. & Pritchard, A.J.	**Sensors and Controls in the Analysis of Distributed Systems**
Exton, H.	**Multiple Hypergeometric Functions and Applications**
Exton, H.	**Handbook of Hypergeometric Integrals**
Exton, H.	***q*-Hypergeometric Functions and Applications**
Faux, I.D. & Pratt, M.J.	**Computational Geometry for Design and Manufacture**
Firby, P.A. & Gardiner, C.F.	**Surface Topology**
Gardiner, C.F.	**Modern Algebra**
Gardiner, C.F.	**Algebraic Structures**
Gasson, P.C.	**Geometry of Spatial Forms**
Goodbody, A.M.	**Cartesian Tensors**
Graham, A.	**Kronecker Products and Matrix Calculus: with Applications**
Graham, A.	**Matrix Theory and Applications for Engineers and Mathematicians**
Graham, A.	**Nonnegative Matrices and Applicable Topics in Linear Algebra**
Griffel, D.H.	**Applied Functional Analysis**
Griffel, D.H.	**Linear Algebra and its Applications: Vol. 1, A First Course; Vol. 2, More Advanced**
Guest, P. B.	**The Laplace Transform and Applications**
Hanyga, A.	**Mathematical Theory of Non-linear Elasticity**
Harris, D.J.	**Mathematics for Business, Management and Economics**
Hart, D. & Croft, A.	**Modelling with Projectiles**
Hoskins, R.F.	**Generalised Functions**
Hoskins, R.F.	**Standard and Nonstandard Analysis**
Hunter, S.C.	**Mechanics of Continuous Media, 2nd (Revised) Edition**
Huntley, I. & Johnson, R.M.	**Linear and Nonlinear Differential Equations**
Irons, B. M. & Shrive, N. G.	**Numerical Methods in Engineering and Applied Science**
Ivanov, L. L.	**Algebraic Recursion Theory**
Johnson, R.M.	**Theory and Applications of Linear Differential and Difference Equations**
Johnson, R.M.	**Calculus: Theory and Applications in Technology and the Physical and Life Sciences**
Jones, R.H. & Steele, N.C.	**Mathematics in Communication Theory**
Jordan, D.	**Geometric Topology**
Kelly, J.C.	**Abstract Algebra**
Kim, K.H. & Roush, F.W.	**Applied Abstract Algebra**
Kim, K.H. & Roush, F.W.	**Team Theory**
Kosinski, W.	**Field Singularities and Wave Analysis in Continuum Mechanics**
Krishnamurthy, V.	**Combinatorics: Theory and Applications**
Lindfield, G. & Penny, J.E.T.	**Microcomputers in Numerical Analysis**
Livesley, K.	**Mathematical Methods for Engineers**
Lord, E.A. & Wilson, C.B.	**The Mathematical Description of Shape and Form**
Malik, M., Riznichenko, G.Y. & Rubin, A.B.	**Biological Electron Transport Processes and their Computer Simulation**
Martin, D.	**Manifold Theory: An Introduction for Mathematical Physicists**
Massey, B.S.	**Measures in Science and Engineering**
Meek, B.L. & Fairthorne, S.	**Using Computers**
Menell, A. & Bazin, M.	**Mathematics for the Biosciences**
Mikolas, M.	**Real Functions and Orthogonal Series**
Moore, R.	**Computational Functional Analysis**
Murphy, J.A., Ridout, D. & McShane, B.	**Numerical Analysis, Algorithms and Computation**
Nonweiler, T.R.F.	**Computational Mathematics: An Introduction to Numerical Approximation**
Ogden, R.W.	**Non-linear Elastic Deformations**
Oldknow, A.	**Microcomputers in Geometry**
Oldknow, A. & Smith, D.	**Learning Mathematics with Micros**
O'Neill, M.E. & Chorlton, F.	**Ideal and Incompressible Fluid Dynamics**

Mathematics and its Applications
Series Editor: G. M. BELL,
Professor of Mathematics, King's College London, University of London

O'Neill, M.E. & Chorlton, F. **Viscous and Compressible Fluid Dynamics**
Page, S. G. **Mathematics: A Second Start**
Prior, D. & Moscardini, A.O. **Model Formulation Analysis**
Rankin, R.A. **Modular Forms**
Scorer, R.S. **Environmental Aerodynamics**
Shivamoggi, B.K. **Stability of Parallel Gas Flows**
Srivastava, H.M. & Manocha, L. **A Treatise on Generating Functions**
Stirling, D.S.G. **Mathematical Analysis**
Sweet, M.V. **Algebra, Geometry and Trigonometry in Science, Engineering and Mathematics**
Temperley, H.N.V. **Graph Theory and Applications**
Temperley, H.N.V. **Liquids and Their Properties**
Thom, R. **Mathematical Models of Morphogenesis**
Toth, G. **Harmonic and Minimal Maps and Applications in Geometry and Physics**
Townend, M. S. **Mathematics in Sport**
Townend, M.S. & Pountney, D.C. **Computer-aided Engineering Mathematics**
Trinajstic, N., Nikolic, S., Knop, J.V., Muller, W.R. & Symanski, K. **Computational Chemical Theory: Characterization, Enumeration and Generation of Chemical Structures by Computer Methods**
Twizell, E.H. **Computational Methods for Partial Differential Equations**
Twizell, E.H. **Numerical Methods, with Applications in the Biomedical Sciences**
Vince, A. and Morris, C. **Discrete Mathematics for Computing**
Walton, K., Marshall, J., Gorecki, H. & Korytowski, A. **Control Theory for Time Delay Systems**
Warren, M.D. **Flow Modelling in Industrial Processes**
Webb, J.R.L. **Functions of Several Real Variables**
Wheeler, R.F. **Rethinking Mathematical Concepts**
Willmore, T.J. **Total Curvature in Riemannian Geometry**
Willmore, T.J. & Hitchin, N. **Global Riemannian Geometry**

Statistics, Operational Research and Computational Mathematics
Editor: B. W. CONOLLY,
Emeritus Professor of Mathematics (Operational Research), Queen Mary College, University of London

Abaffy, J. & Spedicato, E. **ABS Projection Algorithms: Mathematical Techniques for Linear and Nonlinear Equations**
Beaumont, G.P. **Introductory Applied Probability**
Beaumont, G.P. **Probability and Random Variables**
Bunday, B. D. **Statistical Methods in Reliability Theory and Practice**
Conolly, B.W. **Techniques in Operational Research: Vol. 1, Queueing Systems**
Conolly, B.W. **Techniques in Operational Research: Vol. 2, Models, Search, Randomization**
Conolly, B.W. **Lecture Notes in Queueing Systems**
Conolly, B.W. & Pierce, J.G. **Information Mechanics: Transformation of Information in Management, Command, Control and Communication**
French, S. **Sequencing and Scheduling: Mathematics of the Job Shop**
French, S. **Decision Theory: An Introduction to the Mathematics of Rationality**
Goult, R.J. **Applied Linear Algebra**
Griffiths, P. & Hill, I.D. **Applied Statistics Algorithms**
Hartley, R. **Linear and Non-linear Programming**
Jolliffe, F.R. **Survey Design and Analysis**
Jones, A.J. **Game Theory**
Kapadia, R. & Andersson, G. **Statistics Explained: Basic Concepts and Methods**
Lootsma, F. **Operational Research in Long Term Planning**
Moscardini, A.O. & Robson, E.H. **Mathematical Modelling for Information Technology**
Moshier, S.L.B. **Methods and Programs for Mathematical Functions**
Norcliffe, A. & Slater, G. **Mathematics of Software Construction**
Oliveira-Pinto, F. **Simulation Concepts in Mathematical Modelling**
Ratschek, J. & Rokne, J. **New Computer Methods for Global Optimization**
Schendel, U. **Introduction to Numerical Methods for Parallel Computers**
Schendel, U. **Sparse Matrices**
Sehmi, N.S. **Large Order Structural Eigenanalysis Techniques: Algorithms for Finite Element Systems**
Sewell, G. **Computational Methods of Linear Algebra**
Sharma, O.P. **Markovian Queues**
Smith, D.K. **Dynamic Programming: A Practical Introduction**
Späth, H. **Mathematical Software for Linear Regression**
Stoodley, K.D.C. **Applied and Computational Statistics: A First Course**
Stoodley, K.D.C., Lewis, T. & Stainton, C.L.S. **Applied Statistical Techniques**
Thomas, L.C. **Games, Theory and Applications**
Vajda, S. **Fibonacci and Lucas Numbers, and the Golden Section**
Whitehead, J.R. **The Design and Analysis of Sequential Clinical Trials**